TRANSPARENCY WAVE
PRAISES & QUOTES

"Exponential technologies such as computation, genomics, robotics, blockchain, sensors and networks are creating a world of radical transparency. Such transparency will transform our world with the potential for increased trust, health, wisdom and abundance. In his book *Transparency Wave*, Paul Pagnato lays out the principles for the revolution ahead."

— Peter H. Diamandis
Founder, XPRIZE & Singularity University,
New York Times Best-Selling author of *Abundance*,
BOLD and *The Future is Faster Than You Think*

"Transparency is one of the most powerful trends in business, a force that is reshaping everything from corporate governance to personal privacy. Paul Pagnato shines a light on this trend — and the result is an illuminating, important read."

— #1 New York Times best-selling author
Daniel H. Pink, *WHEN*, *DRIVE*, and *TO SELL IS HUMAN*

"A truly transformational read that will educate and inspire! Paul strikes many of life's best chords. Motivational, educational and a perfect guide to ride the *Transparency Wave*."

— Dow Jones Barron's
Joe Lanza

"Today, if you're not disrupting yourself, someone else is; your fate is to be either the disrupter or the disrupted. There is no middle ground."

— Best-selling author
Salim Ismail, *Exponential Organizations*

"The Internet is an ongoing experiment. What we're just trying to do is encourage one more of those experiments that aim to deliver a more benevolent future for us all."

— Google, Chief Internet Evangelist
Dr. Vint Cerf, Co-Father of the Internet
and Dr. David Bray, Executive Director at People-Centered Internet

"Pagnato is one of those rare individuals who combines successful business experience with true wisdom. In *Transparency Wave*, he demonstrates how technology is transforming our world and why it needs to be accompanied by radical transparency to reach its full potential. Truly original piece of work. It gave me new insights on success in the tech-driven economy."

— Fidelity Investments
Sanjiv Mirchandani, President

"Pagnato has broken new ground with his daring exposition, *Transparency Wave*. By using his principles, you can create a successful business in any industry...a must-read for today's disruptive business world. It will give you a massive competitive edge!"

— Merrill Lynch Private Bank
Raj Sharma

"I have had the pleasure of working with my friend Paul Pagnato to encourage better financial practices among young people...*Transparency Wave* is a gorgeous book and a real pleasure to read."

— Harvard University
Prof. John Paul Rollert

"It's happening exponentially. It's not just neuroscience anymore—it's neuroscience and physics and big data...It's going to be an entirely different world in the next 20 years."

— New York Times best-selling author
Dr. Lisa Genova, *Still Alice*

"Technologies are being developed that will allow us to see relationships between our behavior and our health on a time scale never before possible."

— Stanford University
Dr. Laura Carstensen

"The importance of transparency in the real world is notable...greater transparency in corporate earnings has a positive effect on the bottom line, making a case for more transparent financial information provided by Corporate America."

— UC Berkeley
Prof. Yaniv Konchitchki

"We're going to see that in transparency. Reluctance—often resistance—at first but once it begins, it will be unstoppable, and everyone everywhere will suddenly be 100% transparent...the speed of adoption will be astonishing."

— Edelman Financial Engines
Ric Edelman, Founder

"A Rosetta Stone for understanding and thriving in our exponential world. This unique take on what it takes to build a world class organization and achieve extraordinary outcomes in business, and in life, is a highly recommended read for all inspired humans."

— Singularity University
Will Weisman, Global Summits

"There's always going to be a market for really smart news. Somebody...is going to figure out a way to monetize accurate reporting."

— University of Virginia
Prof. Wyatt Andrews

"The tsunami of disruption that is transparency in wealth management is more evident every day. The new normal is already under construction by Millennials and Silicon Valley. Pagnato devours its wide-ranging importance. Ignore him at your own risk."

— Institute for the Fiduciary Standard
Knut Rostad, Co-Founder and President

"Every organization should set clear transparency standards as a foundation for customers and employees. From my vantage point, as a customer advocate and true believer in the power of customer-led thinking, the idea of transparency is a natural feature and benefit of a true customer-centered mindset. You are, for sure, raising the bar on leadership."

— Bain & Company
Mike Baxter, Partner

"In an age of deep cynicism, of fake news and reality star celebrities, where the values of trust and integrity are under threat, Paul Pagnato demonstrates how a new wave of transparency, transparency in our business dealings, in our day-to-day relationships and in how we communicate and share information, offers us a very real solution and a new way of operating and thinking to create a better world."

— Barclays Bank
Craig Bond, Former CEO

"What's cool about the crypto space is that it's right at the heart of what transparency gets you. We're going to see decentralized applications that are very hard for us to imagine today...that are going to unlock an exponential level of value."

— Labelbox
Nathana Sharma, General Counsel; Singularity University Faculty

"Paul is a true visionary in our industry. His latest contribution, *Transparency Wave*, provides his insights on the landscape of tomorrow with tangible strategies to help us position our businesses as totally transparent enterprises led by empowered and enthusiastic colleagues."

— CAPTRUST
Fielding Miller, CEO Founder

"Paul Pagnato's *Transparency Wave* is an important work for addressing digital transformations sweeping through industry, media and our overall culture. He explains the 'exponential changes' swirling around us and provides 'a framework with which to tackle future challenges.' This book is essential reading for anyone engaged in strategic initiatives aimed at confronting disruption. Educators, especially those who teach entrepreneurship and leadership, will benefit from introducing these concepts to students seeking coping mechanisms for a world in flux. Pagnato asserts that transparency's inevitability 'changes everything,' but he encourages us to 'enjoy the ride.' His optimistic message is tonic for our times."

— University of Georgia
Professor Keith L. Herndon, Ph.D.

"Leaders in all types of organizations would do well to heed the lessons of *Transparency Wave*. By embedding transparency standards in strategic plans and practicing the 6Ts of Exponential Transparency in every aspect of organizational behavior, transformational benefits will accrue to individuals, to organizations and to society."

— Stevens Institute of Technology
Nariman Farvardin, President

"Just like any other power, AI can be used to create great, valuable things in society. It can also be used to make harmful things and that is an ultimate question...how do we use AI for better-use cases?"

— Labelbox
Manu Sharma, Founder & CEO

"The ideas that Paul Pagnato describes in his book, *Transparency Wave*, will transform the way you see the world and especially the way you lead. In Paul's words, 'Transparency is creating the greatest wealth in history and will continue to unleash wealth creation never seen by mankind.' His book will help you ride the massive Transparency Wave of change, rather than being swamped by it. It is a must read!"

— Best-selling author
Jim Haudan, *The Art of Engagement* and *What are Your Blind Spots?*

"While Executives and Millennials may value transparency, their recognition of the issues and the way that they address them is often dissimilar."

— Florida Atlantic University
Prof. Rainford Knight

"A compelling narrative about true transparency that's both intriguing and inspiring. Simple and deliberate, it shows us how to apply these principles for both personal fulfillment and to make a positive impact on the world."

— Wealth Management UBS®
Patricia Van Kirk

"The 21st century is our biotechnology century, much as a lot of the 20th century was our digital century. We're reading DNA like code."

— BioCurious
Raymond McCauley, Co-Founder & Chief Architect;
Singularity University, Founding Faculty

"Mindfulness strengthens our ability to understand what is happening and how we are relating to it. In writing *Transparency Wave*, Paul has taken this process and made it applicable to both our personal and professional lives in a profound way."

— Author
Rolf Gates, *Meditations from the Mat: Daily Reflections on the Path of Yoga*

TRANSPARENCY WAVE

EXPONENTIAL CHANGES THAT WILL TRANSFORM OUR WORLD

BARRON'S & FORBES TOP ADVISOR
PAUL A. PAGNATO

FOREWORD BY SALIM ISMAIL

TRANSPARENCY
PRESS

transparencywave.com

TRANSPARENCY WAVE
Exponential Changes That Will Transform Our World

Collaborator: Pete Robbins

Book Design: LeAnne Poindexter

Book Developer: Steve Eunpu

Project Manager: Cathy Rieder

Design Support: Paul Fitzgerald

Copy Editing: Jody Amato, Brian Cavanaugh, Paul Pagnato III

Assistant Manager: Jennifer Wappaus

Audio Narration: Paul A. Pagnato, Jr.

Recording Studio: Blue Room Productions

Library of Congress Control Number: 2019955672

Published by Transparency Press

Transparency Wave®, 6Ts of Exponential Transparency™, and
Transparency Changes Everything™ are trademarks of Transparency LLC.

ISBN 978-1-936961-45-0

ISBN 978-1-936961-47-4 (digital)

Printed in the United States of America

10 9 8 7 6 5 4 3 2 1

transparencywave.com

TRANSPARENCY IS HERE, AND IT'S BEAUTIFUL.

PAUL PAGNATO

WITH GRATITUDE

TO MY FAMILY

Thank you for all the love, support and PMA over the last two years. Angie, you are the love of my life, my soulmate and the angel of patience and understanding. Paul, Alaina and Julia you are the best children a father could possibly ask for. Your spirit and soul are the epicenter in each of you. When your spirit is unleashed, you have an abundance of energy and an ability to positively impact all species around you. The odds of you being who you are one in 400 trillion. You were not an accident or some random occurrence. Your life is infinitely precious, purposeful and needed. Let your spirit out and passionately follow what you love to do and what makes you unique. You have the ability and gifts to do the impossible, think the unimaginable and grow indefinitely. My father, mother, sisters and brother thank you for being who you are. I love each and every one of you and had the best childhood ever because of you. To Nancy, my favorite mother-in-law who is always loving, caring and there for me.

TO TRANSPARENCY WAVE TEAM

Steve Eunpu, the best publishing coach on the planet. This book would not be possible without your wisdom and fortitude keeping all of us focused. Pete Robbins, a superstar writer with the unique ability of making dreams a reality. Thank you for your patience, transparency, wit and artful writing. Cathy Rieder, always there for me, day or night, weekday or weekend. You ROCK. LeAnne Poindexter, the best graphic artist in the world. Thank you for creating the most beautifully designed book ever. Your creativity brought life and visualization to every single chapter. Jennifer Wappaus, thank you for always spearheading the next big challenge.

TO PAGNATOKARP TEAM

Every single team member made this book happen. Freeing me up to perform deep research on transparency, interviewing top experts, traveling the world and thinking creatively. Thank you.

TO CONTRIBUTORS

Huge thanks to Salim Ismail, Peter Diamandis, Vint Cerf, Dr. Lisa Genova, Dr. David Bray, Dr. Laura Carstensen, Ric Edelman, Nathana Sharma, Wyatt Andrews, Dr. Rainford Knight, Manu Sharma, Raymond McCauley and Dr. Yaniv Konchitchki. Providing as much time as needed for our interviews and research.

TO MY MENTORS

Profound thank you to the best mentors a writer could possibly ask for: Daniel Pink, Dan Sullivan, Jim Schleckser, Jim Haudan, Dr. Richard Orlando, Ric Edelman, Fielding Miller, Raj Sharma, John Thiel, John Simmons, Carl Meyer, James Hays, Jim Walker, Carol Nevins, Otto Hoernig, and Phil Nolan.

CONTENTS

FOREWORD

The human species has evolved over a span of 200,000 years into a highly technological civilization. The path we have followed is through a large number of incredible transformations and advancements that took place within a series of innovation waves. Some waves lasting thousands of years and some lasting hundreds of years. What is consistent is that one wave always builds upon another until reaching a tipping point. These tipping points have led to the collapse of great civilizations as well as the spawning of new, more advanced civilizations.

With the *Transparency Wave* book, Paul Pagnato takes us through the waves of the past and future, showing how the pace of change and the frequency of new, incoming waves are accelerating. But most importantly, we are at the tipping point of a tsunami that is cresting. That tsunami is bringing us into an era of mind-boggling exponential change. Advancements in areas such as Genomics, Internet of Things, 3D Printing, Blockchain, Artificial Intelligence, Robotics, Energy Storage, Cloud Computing and Big Data are now converging. I frame this group of breakthroughs as '20 Gutenberg Moments', after the societal impact of the printing press a few centuries ago.

What's amazing is that we can harness these advances to solve global challenges around literacy, food, energy, water, longevity, sanitation and more. For example, exactly 200 years ago in 1820, fully 94% of humanity lived in extreme poverty (living on $2 or less in 2011 dollars). The figure today is less than 9% and Bill Gates predicts we will eradicate extreme poverty in this decade. That is a staggering achievement of global economic development.

If we can hop on this new wave, we will leverage exponential technologies and successfully address many of the world's greatest challenges and bring us into a new era. We are just on the edge of an era of abundance of energy, clean water, food, healthcare and education.

But there is an enormous hurdle standing in the way—and that hurdle is **Trust**.

Allow me to elaborate. Consider the idea that almost every business in history is geared around selling scarcity. In fact, for most of human history, if you didn't have scarcity, you didn't have a business. We have seen already a wholesale transition from a scarcity of information to an abundance of information and the destruction of traditional business models (journalism, network television, etc)—what happens as we enter an abundance of energy, transportation, healthcare and education? We need to transition the entire institution of business and commerce from scarcity to abundance.

From an investment perspective, every investor is desperately wanting trust to ensure the security of any investments. The success of any deal at all needs transparency. The way that links to Trust is the following quote from the venerable Jerry Michalski, who famously said "Scarcity equals Abundance minus Trust".

This means the path to abundance lies through trust. And how do we get to Trust?

Transparency. What Paul Pagnato has done in this book is to craft a bridge from the old wave to the new tsunami. He has clearly shown with his 6Ts of Transparency a step-by-step path to Trust that will allow us globally to better harness these 20 Gutenberg Moments.

Imagine if we can use transparency to scale trust globally and what that would do to capital flows and investments all over the world! For example, the noted economist Hernando de Soto has estimated that if we put land titles on a blockchain so there was transparency (and thus security) in the ownership of a piece of land, just that would unleash about $15 trillion into the global economy.

In analyzing the coming Transparency Wave, Paul interviewed top experts from academia at Singularity University, Stanford, Harvard, Berkeley and the University of Virginia. He interviewed industry leaders in Artificial Intelligence, Machine Learning, Blockchain Technologies,

Longevity, Wealth Management, and the Internet of Things. He interviewed best-selling authors like Daniel Pink and Lisa Genova. Learn how the convergence of great minds, great technologies and great insights are all leading to the most extraordinary time in human history.

The Transparency Wave can be feared or embraced. Those learning to achieve exponential transparency will unleash exponential growth, wealth, quality of life and impact never seen before. Embracing transparency leads to a positive mental attitude, longevity, and abundance. In this book, Paul eloquently teaches all of us the six steps to exponential transparency and with that unlocks the keys to successfully riding the Transparency Wave to new heights.

An economy like that can happen, and Paul has identified the key fulcrum to ensure that it will. I'm extremely excited to watch the paradigm of Transparency get implemented.

Get ready for the ride of your life!!!

— **Salim Ismail**
Best-selling author of *Exponential Organizations* and
Exponential Transformation, Founder OpenExO and ExO Works,
Founding Executive Director at Singularity University

"In the end, it's not the years in your life that count. **It's the life in your years.**"

Abraham Lincoln

About The Author

Paul A. Pagnato is CEO Founder at PagnatoKarp, a wealth management firm based in Reston, Virginia. Paul began in business as a microbiologist, working collaboratively with NASA and McDonnell Douglas to search for life in outer space. He grew up an avid researcher and fossil collector, overturning stones everywhere he could to learn lessons from the past. He has amassed a huge museum-worthy fossil collection, including dinosaur eggs, prehistoric sea floors, and the largest shark jaw ever found. Happiest on the water, Paul spent ten years on the professional bass fishing circuit chasing every fisherman's dream. Never one to sit still, Paul also competed in football, baseball, basketball and skateboarding and even placed second in the World AAU National Power Lifting Championship. Today, he is a yoga certified expert, practicing daily mindful meditation and exploring new ways to positively impact the world.

Paul holding large mouth bass during his career as a professional bass fisherman.

Paul joined the financial industry over 27 years ago to help families manage their wealth. Without a background in finance, he started as a true novice, ultimately spending 19 years with Merrill Lynch and founding the Washington, DC Private Banking and Investment Office. When the 2008 financial crisis revealed massive conflicts of interest in the industry, Paul's focus turned to establishing a new golden standard—Transparency. He put his research skills to work and met directly with hundreds of industry leaders, including the SEC, Department of Labor, and Institute for the Fiduciary Standard. The outcome led to the creation of a new kind of financial company, one founded squarely on standards of transparency. That company is PagnatoKarp.

PagnatoKarp now has over $4.8 billion assets under advisement[1] and Paul is a top-ranked financial advisor by Barron's and Forbes[2], as well as a frequent media contributor to The Wall Street Journal, CNBC, Fox Business, Bloomberg, Reuters, CNN and The Street.

Paul's biggest passion is giving back and believes transparency is the key. Together with family and friends, he empowers organizations aimed at improving literacy, health, humanity and wealth, both locally and worldwide.

A firm believer that exponential technologies will shape the future, Paul is a Singularity University Ambassador and international speaker helping prepare leaders to solve urgent world problems. He also founded the TrueFiduciary® Institute, a nonprofit aimed at financial education and positively impacting our next-generation. Together with Barron's In Education, his goal is to increase financial literacy and

PagnatoKarp gives back in partnership with Homes of Hope in the Dominican Republic.

TrueFiduciary®

To positively impact one million student lives through financial well-being.

wealth transparency at the earliest age. Paul volunteers his time with numerous organizations including Feeding America, Operation Gratitude, and Walter Reed National Military Medical Center, and even built several Homes of Hope in the Dominican Republic to help families in need.

A travel buff, Paul has seen the far reaches of technology into remote regions of the world and is eager to inspire transparency as a path to growth. A speaker at international summits, national conferences, and top universities, Paul's advocacy for transparency includes speaking engagements with the People-Centered Internet Coalition, cofounded by Vint Cerf, Google's Chief Internet Evangelist and "One of the Fathers of the Internet", as well as at top universities including Stanford, Berkeley, the University of Virginia, Georgetown University, University of Maryland, George Mason University and Florida Atlantic University. Paul is Advisory Council Member for Stanford Center on Longevity. Paul serves on the board of directors for Envel, Institute for the Fiduciary Standard, Florida Atlantic University Foundation, INOVA Health System and Pinstriped Prospects.

TRANSPARENCY CHANGES EVERYTHING !!

From Paul's Collection:

(L) One of the largest shark teeth ever found, over 7 inches. Found in Savanah River, GA.

(R) Largest great white shark jaw ever found. From Chile, two million years old.

TRANSPARENCY WAVE

Introduction

Almost every email I send is concluded with a simple three letter acronym: **PMA**. It stands for "**Positive Mental Attitude**," and it's a reminder to all of my mentality.

Some people tease me about my relentless positivity. Some think that it's an act.

Please be assured, it is no act.

As an unrepentant optimist, I believe we have a huge amount of control over the outcomes that we experience. On the occasions when we fail—and we all fail constantly throughout our lifetimes—by remaining positive and trying to learn from those speed bumps, we accelerate growth. Success is failure turned inside out.

Transparency— being vulnerable, open, authentic, and real—is the wave of the future and of successful organizations. An inability to be transparent with ourselves allows our failures to self-realize. Without transparency, you can justify or rationalize anything. In fact, I'll show you how the **6Ts of Exponential Transparency—Transparency Standards, Terms, Total Accountability, Transparent Cost, Truth, and Trust**—can revolutionize your life and lead to exponential growth.

With transparency, the faster we fail, the faster we obtain the outcome we are seeking. Understanding that reality allows you to undertake a complete change of attitude. Life is an experiment, we are the scientists, and a laboratory of constant learning is what we should strive to create. By having multiple experiments occurring simultaneously and learning to accept "failing fast," we experience a paradigm shift in the way we think. Every result, positive or negative, becomes a building block of our ultimate success.

PMA has changed the trajectory of my life, and I credit it with helping attain my proudest accomplishments and greatest successes while amplifying their magnitude.

Some who previously doubted my sincerity (and perhaps my sanity) are starting to come around. They've seen the benefits that this type of outlook creates, and they've also listened attentively when I've explained why there's every reason in the world to expect the world to become a better place, and to expect our lives to improve accordingly. That reason is the exponential growth of technology that has already started and should accelerate substantially in the next few years.

What do I mean by exponential?

Think of a snowball rolling downhill, growing by leaps and bounds; going from two inches to four inches in diameter as quickly as it went from one to two. After hitting the four-inch mark, it doubles again in the same time frame. Before you know it, if it has enough room in front, it's hundreds, thousands, or a million times bigger than the initial grouping of snowflakes.

The example that brings it home for a lot of people is analyzing a penny that doubles every day. Which would you rather have: $100 a day for 30 days, or start with a penny and then double the amount you get each subsequent day (one cent, then two cents, then four cents, then eight cents and so on) for 30 days?

Most people would intuitively reach for the first choice, but when you do the math, you'll be surprised at how poor of a choice that might be.

$100 a day for 30 days is, of course, $3,000. Not a bad sum for sitting there collecting cash, or so it would seem.

Start with a penny and double it each day. By day ten, you'll receive a whopping $5.12; not even enough to supersize your fries. This option isn't projecting to be the better choice, right?

Fear not, that's when the power of exponential growth kicks in! The turning point occurs just a little over a week later, when you'll get $2,621.44 *on a single day*. After that, it gets even crazier, and on day 30 you'll get over $5 million. 30 days is all it took to make that easy $3,000 look like chump change.

Currently we are at a major turning point in the historical development of technology. Certainly, there have been other major shifts driven by technology, and each one makes multiple others possible. That's the snowball effect.

In subsequent chapters, I'm going to highlight some of the areas where the most exciting evolution is occurring through transparency and exponential growth. In some cases, the advances are so complex that they can be tough to comprehend. In areas like longevity, artificial intelligence, and digital assets, I'll quote experts who will say things that seem unlikely or even preposterous, but these brilliant thinkers are willing to stake their careers, reputations, and bank accounts on them. Their certainty that we're at the "knee of the curve" of exponential growth is most exciting, and hopefully that excites you too. My cohorts

WOULD YOU RATHER...

Get $100 Per Day for 30 Days?

Start with a PENNY and then DOUBLE the amount you get each subsequent day for 30 Days?

$3,000

$5,000,000

1 Penny = $1,000

> ## IF YOU CAN IMAGINE IT, **IT CAN BECOME REALITY.**

and sources are going to make some predictions that will seem ridiculous, and that's why I'm so positive about the future. We are truly at a *Field of Dreams* crossroads in human history where if you can imagine it, it can become reality.

Before taking a deep dive into some of these more complex matters, here are some real-world examples that enhance my confidence in this outlook. If you think about how quickly our world has changed in most of our lifetimes, whether you're a senior citizen or a Millennial, it becomes evident that the rate of change is accelerating.

Take, for instance, the automobile. When my grandparents got their first car, it had a radio and used a combustion engine that ran on gasoline. It rode on round tires (remember the wheel, introduced in 3,500 BCE?). When I got my first car, it looked more aerodynamic, had better gas mileage, and was slightly more reliable, but it was essentially the same technology and operated the same way. With both types of vehicles, most accidents were the result of operator error.

Today I drive a Tesla, which has a 370+ mile range on electricity, with no gasoline needed. It has sensors that handle hundreds of inputs and, where allowed, it can drive itself. In fact, studies have shown that self-driving cars of this caliber result in fewer accidents. They can absorb and process relevant information more quickly than the human brain, sifting out distractions and making better decisions.

Would my grandparents have been able to conceive of a self-driving car back in their day? Perhaps, but it would've seemed like something out of a science-fiction movie. This leads me to believe that the changes to vehicles that we'll see during my lifetime will make these Tesla features seem like child's play.

Don't believe me about the "science-fiction" claims? If you're old enough to remember the 1960s television show *Get Smart*, you may recall that agent Maxwell Smart wowed us with his "shoe phone." It was literally a telephone inside the sole of his shoe. When he wanted to make or receive a call on the sly, he'd slip it off his foot, put it to his ear, and communicate furtively. "Yeah, right!" we thought. How could a telephone be condensed down to such a small package? How could it be made wireless? Who could afford the long-distance charges that it would rack up?

A generation later, virtually everyone has a cell phone. They went from the "brick" of the 1980s to the flip phones of the late 1990s, to the first iPhone, and then to the point where almost everyone always has a smartphone with them. Not only is it a better and more portable phone than its predecessors (without the long-distance charges!), it has replaced multiple other devices, such as your GPS, camera, and alarm clock.

Today I wear an Apple Watch, which not only is far smaller than anything Maxwell Smart could have dreamed of, but it does so much more, including accurately monitoring my progress toward fitness goals. It's waterproof, too, so I can participate in a conference call while I'm burning calories on my stand-up paddleboard.

Thus, as the technology grows by leaps and bounds, it's not only making us more efficient, it also aids longevity. It now takes half as long to do twice as much, and those benefits are spreading at an unheard-of pace.

On a fishing trip in 2017, a group of us traveled to a remote region of the Amazon basin. Much of the time spent there was at least fifty to one-hundred miles from the nearest road. One evening, our guide asked us if we wanted to visit a traditional village. Jumping at the chance, we went in with trepidation, figuring that they would be primitive and wary.

Quite to the contrary, virtually every one of them had a smartphone. Five years ago, they might not have had a clue about American music or geography or world events, but now they are as connected as anyone in a major city worldwide.

Gordon Moore, the cofounder of Fairchild Semiconductor and Intel, predicted in 1965 that the number of components of an integrated circuit would double each year for at least another decade. In 1975, he said that it would double every other year. While various theorists have subsequently disagreed on the exact pace of "Moore's Law," it has been extrapolated to technology matters generally to mean that technology will continue to get better at a rapid pace, while the size and cost of these advanced items will decrease. Think of the telephone, television, and computer that you own today and compare them to what you used a decade or two ago, and you'll see what I mean.

These advances in technology don't just make our lives better; they have the potential to make them longer and healthier. For this, I'll share a very meaningful personal story. My daughter suffers from celiac disease, which results from a reaction to gluten. From the second to fourth grades, she didn't gain any weight at all. Today, even with strict adherence to a gluten-free diet, she occasionally still suffers from complications and pain. For example, she has weaker-than-normal bone density because her intestines do not absorb important nutrients as they should.

As a result, six years ago, she had hip surgery at a world-renowned medical facility. We sought out the top doctor in the field, using the best available technology, and she was a perfect patient. Even though the surgery was a success, she still experienced some discomfort afterward. She went through a lengthy rehabilitation and was sidelined for a period of weeks.

THESE **ADVANCES IN TECHNOLOGY** DON'T JUST MAKE OUR LIVES BETTER; THEY HAVE THE POTENTIAL TO **MAKE THEM LONGER AND HEALTHIER.**

Fast-forward to 2018, and my daughter needed another similar surgery. The necessity and the pain were just as substantial as the first time, but the process was much less invasive and debilitating. The surgeons were in and out in a far shorter time, with new, less-scarring tools, and her recovery was substantially quicker.

Astonishingly, just one week later she was driving, and shortly thereafter she was on a plane to an active vacation on the beaches of the Dominican Republic. We urged her to be cautious, but at the same time we knew that she was safe and healthy.

Hopefully she will not need to undergo similar procedures in the future. If she does the procedure will certainly be safer and more effective than it is today.

This expansion in technology has been turbo-boosted by the increasingly widespread dissemination of information. Today you have at your fingertips more immediate access to anything you want—from encyclopedias and sports scores to open-source software. Remember those guys with the smartphones in the Amazon? One of them could have discovered the cure for cancer or some such other major breakthrough. A decade ago, they wouldn't have been able to take from, or contribute to, the information superhighway. Today they are driving in its fast lane. We're substantially closer to maximizing the potential of the earth's human capital.

The democratization of information extends to all our major scientific and technological improvements, but perhaps the best way to understand it is through basketball. The National Basketball Association (NBA) was founded in 1946, and the league signed its first television deal in 1953. Not every game was recorded or broadcast, which means that some of that early history lives on only in the history books.

Several decades later, in the 1970s and 1980s, even some of the NBA Finals games—the biggest events of the year in one of our country's four major sports—were still televised on tape delay. Many of us did not have cable television during that time period, which left us with four or five channels, making their prime-time real estate a valuable commodity.

Even though networks had the rights to the NBA Finals, they elected to show other programming instead. If you were a fan of one of the teams competing, you had to either listen on the radio or wait until later to find out what happened.

I recall in 1980, when I was a teenager, that Kareem Abdul-Jabbar of the Lakers got injured during an NBA Finals game against the 76ers, and in a critical Game 6 on the road, rookie Ervin "Magic" Johnson played all five positions. He tallied 42 points, 15 rebounds, and seven assists on route to the championship trophy and the series MVP award. Unless you attended the game or lived in one of the competing teams' television markets, you didn't see it in real time.

A few years later, cable television became ubiquitous in American life, and Americans learned what "on demand" truly means. It might require a little cash outlay, but you could watch any major sporting event as it happened, from anywhere in the country. Later, you could even choose your choice of broadcast teams. Even later, it became possible to watch from your choice of devices, everything from an increasingly cheaper big-screen television to a variety of mobile screens.

As I write these pages, the cable television technology that made that revolution possible is becoming antiquated, replaced by a variety of streaming services. Some will survive, and they too will eventually be replaced by better media. The trend is the same—more information, spread more widely. Some actions of the NBA players of the 40's, 50's, and 60's exist only in the minds of the remaining people who were there. We have some footage of the players from the 70's, 80's, and 90's, but by no means is it comprehensive.

By the time LeBron James ends his career, however, you will be able to see every play he's ever made, whether he had the ball or was away from it, from multiple angles. There will be computer simulations that'll show how he would've reacted under different circumstances or with different teammates. You'll have a LeBron hologram in your living room, wearing any one of a number of uniforms.

My only fear in writing this book is that the rate at which this technology is evolving will make some of my examples seem antiquated just a few years from now. We assumed Blockbuster would be a permanent fixture, but YouTube and Netflix made Blockbuster expendable. What will replace YouTube and Netflix?

HOW CAN YOU **PREPARE FOR A FUTURE** THAT IS, BY DEFINITION, INCONCEIVABLE NOW?

If you're a business owner, these are the types of questions you need to ask yourself. How can you prepare for a future that is, by definition, inconceivable now? The same holds true even if you don't run a business. How do you ensure that you retain lifetime employability in case your career sector is eliminated? Furthermore, **if you're going to live to be 100, 120, or 150 years old, how do you take care to preserve both quality of life and financial stability?**

All these questions keep some people up at night. I've certainly spent hours pondering them myself, and they make me excited more than nervous. Why? Precisely because of the democratization of information that I've outlined above.

At a time when many people rue the hyper-partisanship and instability that seem to characterize our political and social lives, I'm confident that the increased transparency of information will work to make this a better place. If we put more information in more hands and minds, we can overcome anything that confronts us. Knowledge is power, and increasingly that power is not concentrated among just a few elites.

In 2017, it was revealed by Equifax that they'd suffered a massive data breach that potentially compromised the information for tens of millions of people. Since then, social media companies, including Facebook, have come under fire for failing to prevent outside parties from accessing the data of 50 million users, potentially compromising the political integrity of the United States.

Despite examples of cases where extreme transparency may have resulted in a negative consequence, that should not discourage us from moving toward a more transparent society. Of course, there are limits to the amount of transparency we should encourage. If the military were to publish their plans for all to see, it would defeat the purpose of their efforts.

With that said, when we limit the exchange of accurate and meaningful information, we often correspondingly limit our potential. Conversely, when we operate as an "open book," the results can foster exponential growth.

> WHEN WE OPERATE AS AN "OPEN BOOK," THE RESULTS CAN FOSTER **EXPONENTIAL GROWTH.**

Back in my 20's, I worked for a major brokerage house. A large part of my time was spent cold-calling potential sales leads and, not surprisingly, a lot of their responses were the telephonic equivalent of getting the door slammed in my face. Nevertheless, I was persistent and hungry to acquire new business.

One day, while pitching a prospect, rather than hanging up the phone, they seemed interested in what was being presented, so we scheduled a meeting. Rather than heading home to my wife and newborn child, we planned to meet at my office one evening after hours.

Once seated, they explained their desire to start saving for retirement. We poured over their finances, options, and the amount that could be allocated in their current financial situation.

It quickly became clear that the smartest way for them to start would be through a tax-advantaged plan administered by their employer. If they took the advice that was transparently provided any sort of profit or commission would go out the window. But it was the right thing to do.

They called shortly thereafter, having conferred with their boss and figured out that they had no corporate retirement plan. Rather than investing a small amount of cash with me, which would have provided a small profit, they instead extended an invitation to assist in setting up and administering a plan for the entire company. By being transparent, I'd given up the hope of a short-term profit, but the result was beyond my wildest dreams. They became my first million-dollar client, and they remain with me today, many years later, having grown to over a billion dollars in revenue.

While realizing that not all situations involving transparency are that clear-cut, nor do all of them resolve themselves in the same "happily ever after" fashion, I think of that experience often.

What would have changed if I had not been fully transparent?

Would I be in the same position I'm in today?

How can I better integrate transparency into my life and career?

Whenever meeting a subject matter expert in an area that seems primed for exponential growth in the near future, I try to ask them similar questions. The inspiration for this book was to pick the brains of visionaries on how to marry technology and transparency to keep both the short-term stability and the long-term viability of our world in motion.

After speaking to those experts, I remain more optimistic about our future than ever before. With the greatest minds of several generations considering these questions, we have the tools to solve even the most complex problems.

TRANSPARENCY CHANGES EVERYTHING !!

PART ONE
TRANSPARENCY IS HERE

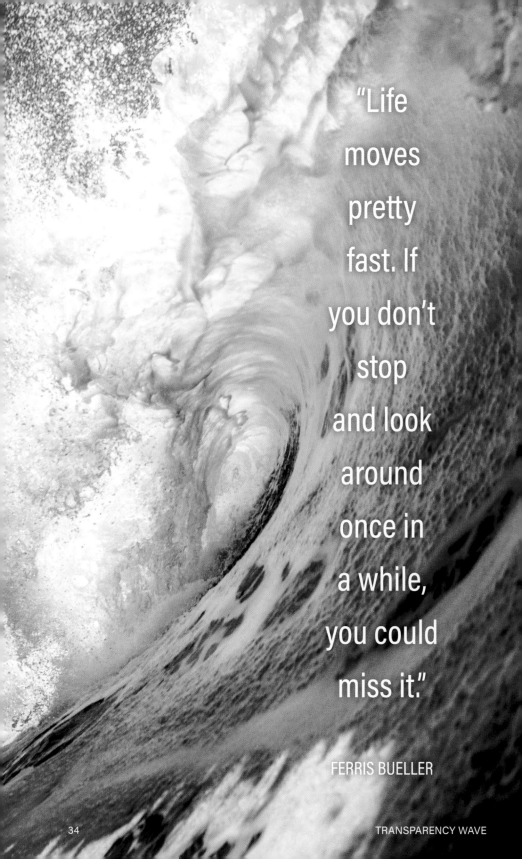

"Life moves pretty fast. If you don't stop and look around once in a while, you could miss it."

FERRIS BUELLER

CHAPTER 1
Waves of the Past and Future

Ferris Bueller, the title character of the 1986 John Hughes film *Ferris Bueller's Day Off*, broke down the fourth wall and told viewers: "Life moves pretty fast. If you don't stop and look around once in a while, you could miss it."

Of course, he was right.

Our world moves more quickly every day—we have more obligations, more passwords to remember, and sometimes fewer opportunities to stop and smell the roses. The ongoing exponential growth in the world of technology has made keeping up both a challenge and an opportunity.

If you miss either of them, you could be further back from where you started. On the flip side, if you capitalize upon both the challenges and the opportunities, the world can be your oyster. With the democratization of technology, nothing is beyond our reach. If you can dream it, you can achieve it.

While a firm believer that it is critical to be "present" in every moment of life, I am also motivated by the concepts of "waves." Think of the challenges in your life as oceans to cross. If you jump in, point your toes, and start swimming, all sorts of things are going to hinder your progress. Wind and tides can push against you. A faulty sense of direction might make your path less Point A to Point B, and more of a maze or a zigzag. You're going to get tired out before you reach your destination. But if you harness the power of the waves—even a single wave—you can coast straight to your target with your eyes focused and your energy preserved.

Alvin Toffler

Futurist author Alvin Toffler is probably the most famous theorist to discuss the importance of waves, each one pushing obstacles out of the way. A decade after the publication of his best-selling book *Future Shock*, Toffler wrote *The Third Wave*, which described societal transitions over the past several centuries. His first wave involved agricultural developments, the second was the Industrial Revolution, and the third was post-industrial society. In each case, the "waves" had substantial impacts not just on the way we produced our goods and earned a living, but also on family and societal structures, with numerous effects rippling outward.

Toffler claimed that the third wave started in the 1950s and is ongoing (Toffler passed away in 2016). Many of his predictions, particularly those about advancing technology and connectivity, were strikingly accurate. He also coined the phrase "anticipatory democracy," which stressed that as technology advanced, top-down bureaucratic institutions would be replaced by a more democratic, people-centered society. As a result of his groundbreaking work, he has often been cited as a prime influence on other successful innovators, including Ted Turner, Carlos Slim, and J.D. Power.

Steve Case, a founder of America Online (AOL), one of the companies heavily responsible for bringing the Internet age to a wide swath of society, often cited Toffler as a major influence. "But it was something that was intriguing to me," Case told *Business Insider* in 2018,[1] "and I just thought it would be important, and I wanted to be part of it, and wanted to figure out ways to popularize it." Case likewise defined the Internet's rise in terms of waves.

"To Steve Case, AOL marked the first wave of the Internet, the rise of social media marked the second wave, and now we're at the forefront of the third wave," Toffler said. "Case predicts that Silicon Valley will lose some of its central importance in this next wave of Internet companies, where the "Internet of Things" essentially becomes the Internet of everything and revolutionizes industries like agriculture and transportation."

Part of Toffler's thesis was that each new wave kills the last one. When the third wave takes over, he posited, the result would be "the death of industrialization." In thinking about the future, and the growth that is both occurring and will continue to occur, I too have adopted waves as the framework for these, but rather than seeing one wave as separate from the next, or killing the next, **I see them as part of a continuum**. Two waves in the ocean, although they may be hundreds of miles apart, are connected by a vast, unbroken amount of water. There is life beneath them, impacted by their activities, and in return impacting the waves. It's a massive interrelated ecosystem. One wave doesn't replace another so much as build upon it, and when it crashes against a distant shore, it has an impact there, as well as building a landing pad for the ones behind it.

> "TO STEVE CASE, AOL MARKED THE FIRST WAVE OF THE INTERNET, THE RISE OF SOCIAL MEDIA MARKED THE SECOND WAVE, AND **NOW WE'RE AT THE FOREFRONT OF THE THIRD WAVE.**"
>
> ALVIN TOFFLER

I am heavily indebted to Toffler's concept of waves as a launching point, and many of my friends and mentors are too, including Raymond McCauley, a brilliant scientist, Chair of Digital Biology at Singularity University, and cofounder and Chief Architect for BioCurious, the hackerspace for biotech. McCauley stated at a 2019 Singularity Global Summit in Mexico that, "The 21st century is our biotechnology century, much as a lot of the 20th century was our digital century, and I really just think we're still about halfway through getting started with that."

Steve Case has borrowed Toffler's title for a book of his own, in which he argues that the third wave of the Internet is upon us, "a period in which entrepreneurs will vastly transform major 'real world' sectors like health, education, transportation, energy, and food—and in the process change the way we live our daily lives." I agree with him that technology is a huge driver here, and that entrepreneurs and leaders will need to anticipate, understand, and harness it moving forward. Nevertheless, technology alone does not get us to where we need to be. As we internalize recent exponential growth and prepare for next steps, we need to anticipate how to maximize its benefits and minimize its social costs.

In thinking about that challenge, think in terms of waves of advancement. The first wave was the **COMMUNICATION WAVE**. The second wave was the **DIGITAL WAVE**. The third wave, the one that no one seems to be talking about, is the **TRANSPARENCY WAVE**. How does that differ from

THREE WAVES OF INNOVATION

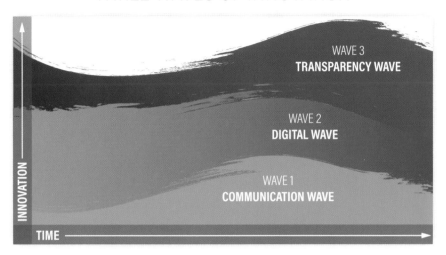

the way other thought leaders have conceptualized our progress? If you look at their models, you see in each instance that changing technology forms the base of it, but there's nothing new about transparency itself. It has been a social good since the first cavemen built a society. If they were transparent about their needs and abilities and circumstances, the whole was much more than the sum of its parts. When one of them hid some critical fact or possession, though, it might have provided him some short-term gain, but at a long-term cost.

We need to think about the long term. We need to be ready to harness the powers presented to us, but also remain vigilant so that we can pivot from the top of the wave if it looks like it's going to come crashing down prematurely. There is a wave that will deliver us to where we need to be; we just need to take a good look at where it is going.

TRANSPARENCY CHANGES EVERYTHING !!

PERSPECTIVES

CHAPTER 1 | WAVES OF THE PAST
AND FUTURE

WHY **IT MATTERS:**

- Either ride the wave or get knocked down by it. If you ride, steer it in any direction, but if you get knocked down, others are lined up in fast succession—and won't stop just because you're trying to catch your breath.

- The future is coming with intensity, velocity, and more opportunity than ever— but there are also pitfalls. Come at the world with open arms and a lens of truthfulness.

ADVICE:

- Attitude is everything. No one can avoid failures, great or small, but character—and success—are revealed by how you deal with setbacks. Some of your greatest achievements will be the direct result of your greatest setbacks.

  - Success is failure turned inside out.
  - Fail early, often and forward.

- Embrace these principles through Positive Mental Attitude (PMA). The first negative thought paves the way to failure, so don't let it affect your attitude. If it sneaks by, beat it back and replace it with positivity.

at·ti·tude
/'adə't(y)ōōd/
a settled way of thinking or feeling about someone or something, typically one that is reflected in a person's behavior.

TAKE**AWAYS:**

- There will be more innovation in the next ten years than in the last hundred—technological advances in all fields will be mind-blowing and consequential for us all. We may not know in real time which will be most important, but the markets will sort the best of the best and spawn further benefits.

- If the mind can conceive it, we can achieve it. Attitude is everything and the only limitations are those we place upon ourselves. A cure for cancer? Possible in the short term. Curing world hunger? Absolutely. Artificial intelligence that makes life easier, more productive, and more enjoyable? Just the tip of the iceberg!

- Our human obligation is to help others—we gain the greatest happiness and satisfaction by fulfilling the needs of others. It's a two-way street and invariably those who seek to hijack innovations meant for the greater good, to use for selfish purposes, will undermine themselves.

ACTION STEPS:

- Have no regrets—pursue your dreams. Life moves fast so there's no time to waste. Figure out what gives your life meaning and work toward those goals every day.

- Life is a journey—enjoy the trip. Ride the wave as if your life depends on it, because it does. Better to view things from the top than get pounded into the sand.

- Seek the flourishing of others—a rising tide lifts all boats. The journey is better if you lift others up to the top of the wave with you.

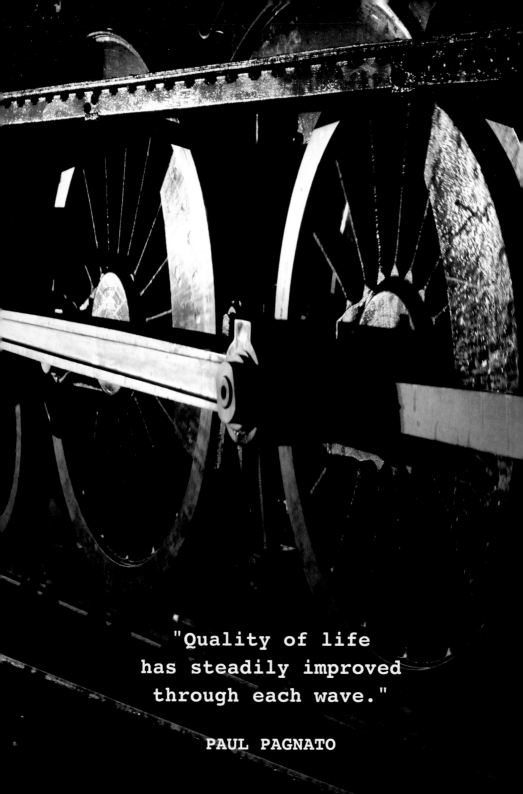

"Quality of life
has steadily improved
through each wave."

PAUL PAGNATO

TRANSPARENCY WAVE

CHAPTER 2

The Communication Wave

The history books generally tell us with a high level of certainty that the Industrial Revolution started in the mid-1700s and lasted another hundred years or so. It moved from country to country as developed countries looked to industrialize and dominate less-developed areas. As it advanced and spread, it truly changed every aspect of day-to-day life. Instead of living on the family farm, isolated from others, you moved to an urban environment and worked in a factory.

Of course, there were advantages and disadvantages to industrialization, and many volumes can and have been written about them, but overall productivity, income, and standard of living rose as the result of the technological changes. A family no longer needed to make its own clothes or find a way to power its own tools. Products made of higher-grade materials could be

SOURCE: The IK Workshop Society at The IK Foundation: Power Loom Weaving – From: 'History of the cotton manufacture in Great Britain' in 1835 by Edward Baines. (Courtesy of: Wellcome Library, London no. L0011293).

purchased and transported by railway, leaving individuals, families, and communities better able to apportion labor and produce those items that they could make best. Quality of life improved. The average work week went from 77 hours, seven days a week working on a farm, to a 40-hour work week over five days. In 1869, President Ulysses S. Grant issued a proclamation that guaranteed an eight-hour workday without a decrease in pay for government workers. By 1905, the eight-hour workday was common practice in the printing industry. Then, in 1926, Henry Ford issued a five-day, 40-hour work week for all Ford Motor workers.

History books accurately convey that those technological and societal changes had a massive and ongoing impact on the world at large, but in another respect, they got it wrong. The true Industrial Revolution didn't wait until the 1700s to commence. If anything, the groundwork had been laid 300 years earlier, when Gutenberg started with the printing press. The circumstances that allowed it to happen were the first part of that wave—increased intellectualism and capitalism, plus foundational technologies like paper and ink that made it possible. The wave continued after Gutenberg brought his invention out and continues today.

HOW DID THE PRINTING PRESS CHANGE THE WORLD?

It served as a spark point for further developments. It democratized knowledge so that subsequent inventors, developers, and thought leaders didn't need to "re-invent the wheel" each time they looked to create something new. Instead, there was a wealth of information at their fingertips, recorded to be used again and again.

Books that took weeks or months or years to reprint could be mass-produced in a small percentage of that time, without errors or inconsistencies, and eventually at a fraction of the cost.

EUROPEAN OUTPUT OF PRINTED BOOKS (CA 1450-1800*)

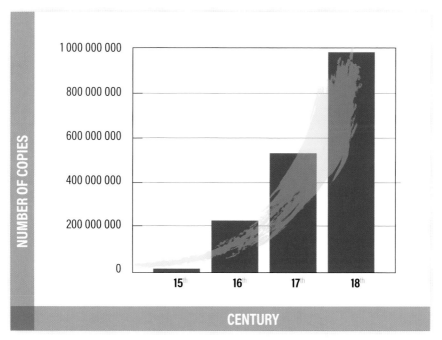

*Without Southeast Europe (Ottoman realm) and Russia

Data from: Buringh, Eltjo; van Zanden, Jan Luiten: "Charting the "Rise of the West": Manuscripts and Printed Books in Europe, A Long-Term Perspective from the Sixth through Eighteenth Centuries", The Journal of Economic History, Vol. 69, No. 2 (2009), pp. 409–445 (417, table 2)

Indeed, the introduction of the printing press was so important because knowledge equals power, and now knowledge could reach a wider and more diverse audience. Education, and specifically the ability to read, became a means of lifting one's self, family, and community out of a rut and into another level of existence. It is the reason that slave owners, autocrats, tyrants and despots throughout history have sought to limit information and marginalize intellectuals— because knowledge, once obtained, is a vehicle not only for empowerment but for change as well. If you have it, you can exercise tremendous authority over others. Used improperly, it can be a negative, but if employed the right way, it can spur additional positive change.

EVERY TWO DAYS WE CREATE AS MUCH INFORMATION AS WE DID FROM THE DAWN OF CIVILIZATION UP UNTIL 2003.

Today, the amount of information we create is almost beyond comprehension. I recently read that, in modern times, every two days we create as much information as we did from the dawn of civilization up until 2003.[1]

So, if we consider the printing press Wave 1A, and the 18th-century developments Wave 1B, we're left with a long but gradual period of improvements, punctuated by short spurts of time in which new developments spurred things forward rapidly. It's not a classic "hockey stick"-shaped model of exponential growth, but rather a 400-year, forward-moving process with more jagged upward ticks at semi-regular intervals.

As we move forward into other waves, though, we see the timeframes collapse. What took the Communication Wave 400 years to develop completely is condensed down to about 50 years in the next wave, the Digital Wave. We can expect subsequent waves—specifically, the Transparency Wave, which is entering its growth period as I write this

THE FIRST WAVE OF INNOVATION: COMMUNICATION WAVE

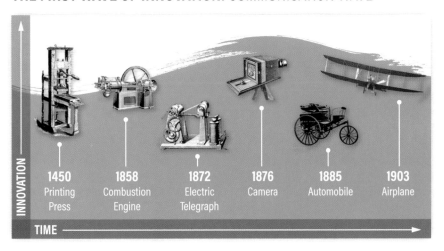

in 2019—to progress even faster. That's why we need to "stop and look around," as Ferris Bueller implored, but we can't take our eyes off forward progress.

TRANSPARENCY CHANGES EVERYTHING !!

PERSPECTIVES

CHAPTER 2 | THE COMMUNICATION WAVE

THE PRINTING PRESS SERVED AS A SPARK POINT FOR FURTHER DEVELOPMENTS. IT DEMOCRATIZED KNOWLEDGE SO THAT SUBSEQUENT INVENTORS, DEVELOPERS, AND THOUGHT LEADERS DIDN'T NEED TO "REINVENT THE WHEEL" EACH TIME THEY LOOKED TO CREATE SOMETHING NEW.

com·mu·ni·ca·tion

/kə'myo'onə'kāSH(ə)n/

the imparting or exchanging of information or news.

WHY IT MATTERS:

- History teaches us that change is inevitable, change is good, and we need to embrace it.

- Knowledge equals power.

ADVICE:

- Stop and look around, but always lean forward.

- Knowledge is a vehicle for both empowerment and change.

TAKEAWAYS:

- The printing press enabled people not only to communicate, but to educate themselves as well. The amount of information we create daily is almost beyond comprehension.

ACTION STEPS:

- Welcome change in your daily life.

- Become a lifelong learner.

- Read, read, read!

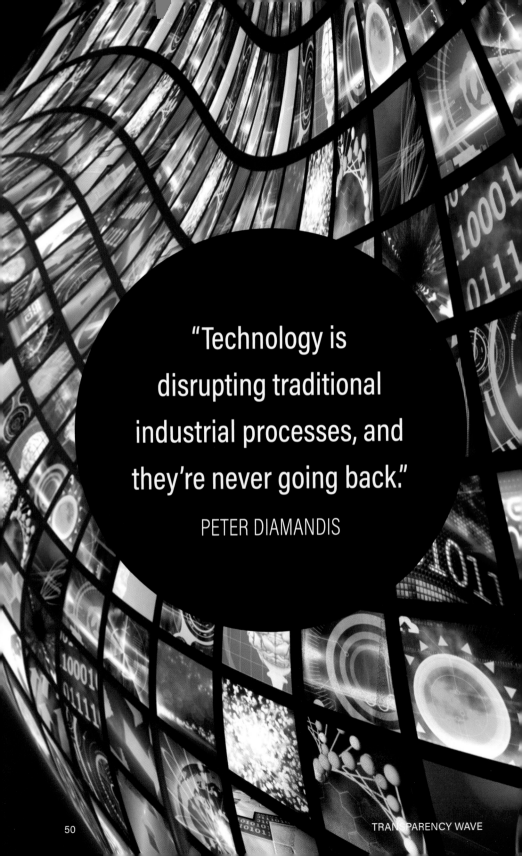

"Technology is disrupting traditional industrial processes, and they're never going back."

PETER DIAMANDIS

CHAPTER 3

The Digital Wave

Like many of my colleagues in their 40's and 50's, my natural tendency is to think of the 1990's as the incubation period for the Internet and the resulting mass digitization of our lives. Quite to the contrary, the Internet was actually born when many of us were in diapers or in elementary school, when Vint Cerf and Bob Kahn (who, with apologies to Al Gore, are the true "Fathers of the Internet"), who worked for the United States government's Defense Advanced Research Project Agency (DARPA), cracked the code of Transmission Control Protocols and Internet Protocols for networking.

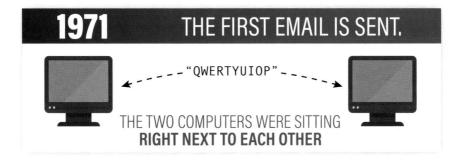

As Cerf and Kahn continue to be lauded for their five decades of monumental advances, both still work diligently to harness the power of digitization, the progress of which seems to move at increasing speeds each year.

THE SECOND WAVE OF INNOVATION: DIGITAL WAVE

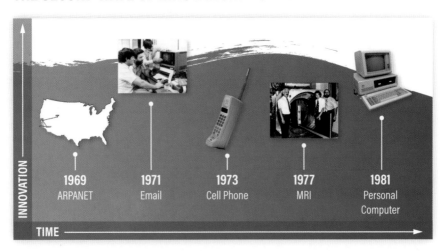

Moore's Law has long been the dominant paradigm or framework by which computing power has been measured. Simply put, Intel cofounder Gordon Moore profoundly stated in the 1960s that "the number of transistors in a dense integrated circuit doubles about every two years."

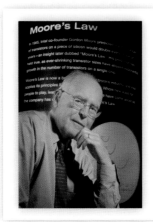

MOORE'S LAW:

"THE NUMBER OF TRANSISTORS IN A DENSE INTEGRATED CIRCUIT DOUBLES ABOUT EVERY TWO YEARS."

GORDON MOORE

While that statement may not be consistently true over the ensuing 50-year period,[1] with the doubling occurring slightly faster or slower during any particular snapshot in time, the general principle holds true: as a result of digitization, we are increasingly able to get more computing power out of smaller packages at a lower cost. That's a win for everybody—in layman's terms, it also reduces the number of devices that you need. Remember your old rotary phone, digital camera, atlas, and Rolodex? They were utilitarian but clunky, and collectively not particularly transportable. Now they're all encased in a single portable telephone that sits in your front pocket. Not only is it substantially smaller than the phone that you had a few years ago, but more importantly, it has exponentially more computing power than NASA used to first put a man on the moon. Your smartphone isn't necessarily disposable, but it's almost guaranteed that in a few months or a few years you'll crave a new one with more and better features, stronger computing power, and other distinct advantages.

It's not just the amount of power you have at your fingertips that makes a difference. It's how it is used to bridge gaps between people, continents, industries, and ideas. Less than 20 years ago—and it seems much more recent to me—the Internet hadn't been fully adopted by much of society, and certainly not around the world. Here in the United States, we were worried about the Y2K phenomenon, which turned out not to be such a big deal. My wife and I actually threw a Y2K party. This made New Year's Eve a little more fun than normal. But since then, the Internet, as a connector, has literally exploded and permeated every facet of our lives. The tools that we take for granted have all emerged since then:

LinkedIn (2003), Facebook (2004), Twitter (2006), WhatsApp (2009)

Instagram (2010), Pinterest (2010), Snapchat (2011)

These technologies and platforms are so entrenched in our lives that many of us can't figure out how we ever lived without them, yet they're all exceptionally new by historical standards. That's emblematic of the compression of the "Waves" we experience throughout history, and you can bet that the next ones will be even faster moving and every bit as transformational.

WRIGHT'S LAW

IS BEING FELT

BY THE PRICING

COLLAPSE FROM

TECHNOLOGY

EFFICIENCIES,

Not many people are familiar with Wright's Law. In a 1936 Journal of Aeronautical Sciences article, Theodore Wright posited that progress increases with experience; each percentage increase in cumulative production in a given industry results in a fixed percentage improvement in production efficiency. He determined while studying airplane manufacturing that for every doubling of airplane production, the labor requirement was reduced by 10–15%. Wright's Law is being felt by the pricing collapse from technology efficiencies. Historically, people would associate price with demand. The more demand for a product, the higher the price. Wright's Law proves that this is inaccurate; just the opposite is occurring. The more

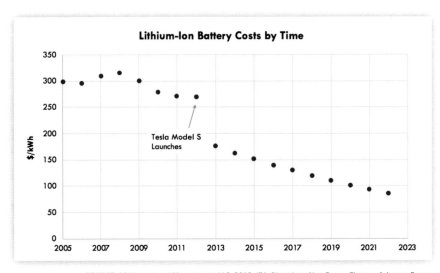

SOURCE: ARK Investment Management LLC, 2018; IEA, Bloomberg New Energy Finance, Avicenne Energy

products sold over Amazon, the lower the price. The more cars Tesla sells, Elon Musk lowers the price. Equity analysts have a difficult time understanding Wright's Law because they have been taught supply and demand in graduate school. "Researchers at MIT and the Santa Fe Institute have found that commonly used formulas for predicting how rapidly technology will advance—notably, Moore's Law and Wright's Law—offer superior approximations of the pace of technological progress."[2]

Of the two, Wright's Law was found to be slightly more accurate than Moore's Law.[3]

Ray Kurzweil, one of the most influential futurists, developed the "Law of Accelerating Returns" to explain our increased rate of advancement. He wrote:

"So, we won't experience 100 years of progress in the 21st century—it will be more like 20,000 years of progress (at today's rate). The 'returns,' such as chip speed and cost-effectiveness, also increase exponentially. There's even exponential growth in the rate of exponential growth."[4]

In my 20's and 30's, envisioning that something like Facebook or Twitter would dominate interpersonal communications and media the way that they do today would have been preposterous. That's what is so exciting about the future, the fact that we may not be able to even envision the next steps—but we can welcome them with open arms and a discerning eye.

> "SO WE WON'T EXPERIENCE 100 YEARS OF PROGRESS IN THE TWENTY-FIRST CENTURY— **IT WILL BE MORE LIKE 20,000, YEARS OF PROGRESS.**"
>
> RAY KURZWEIL
> FOUNDER, SINGULARITY UNIVERSITY

Beyond Moore's Law and its corollaries, how is this era of exponential impacts moving forward?

How are all companies, industries, and institutions moving forward?

My thinking about this topic was changed forever during a presentation by Peter Diamandis at Singularity University's Executive Program. The sign of a true genius is someone who can take a complex and difficult topic and make it simple to understand without sacrificing any accuracy. That's what he did, and it explained the massive growth of companies in multiple industries by breaking them all down into six common transformative characteristics, all of which begin with the letter "D."

The 6Ds of Exponential Organizations are a chain reaction of technological progression, a road map of rapid development that always leads to enormous upheaval and opportunity," Diamandis said*.[5] For now, let's just establish that exponential growth is ongoing. It will receive the fuller treatment that it deserves in a later chapter. The six phases he identified are as follows:

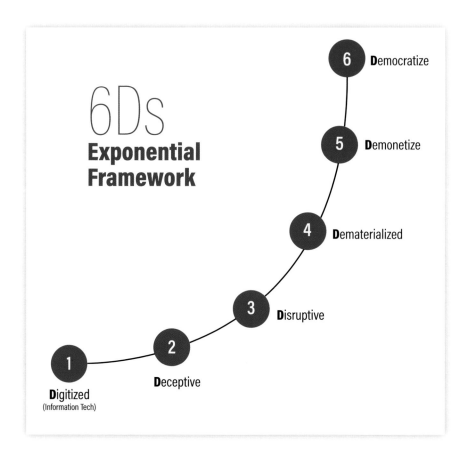

The 1st phase in the process is **DIGITIZATION**. With computing power growing exponentially, there's no industry—from agriculture to media to manufacturing to the arts and beyond—that is exempt from this reality. There is literally an "app" for everything, and they're all at your fingertips. **Steve Wozniak, a cofounder of Apple Computers** and one of the brightest engineers of the modern era, spoke at a recent event I attended hosted by Pepperdine University's business school. Over the course of his celebrated career, Wozniak created many transformational products and concepts including the Mac 2. Unexpectedly, he was quick to name "**applications**" when asked to boil down Apple's single greatest contribution. Over two million apps have been created to date, with the number increasing every day, all directly stemming from Apple's decision to open up their system. Apps consistently become more efficient and advanced, while their ubiquity and cost substantially drop.

"THE SIX DS ARE A CHAIN REACTION OF TECHNOLOGICAL PROGRESSION, A ROAD MAP OF RAPID DEVELOPMENT THAT ALWAYS LEADS TO **ENORMOUS UPHEAVAL AND OPPORTUNITY**."

PETER DIAMANDIS
FOUNDER, SINGULARITY UNIVERSITY

A decade ago, you might've hailed or called for a taxi. These days, virtually no one does that; instead, they digitally summon an Uber. Even the word "Uber" has replaced "taxi" in the common vernacular. The company's success is all because of transparency, which begets a better user experience. In advance, you know which car will pick you up, what brand and model it is, the driver's identity, how much the ride will cost, and exactly where the driver currently is and the route you will take. You no longer need to carry cash, making payment frictionless. In 2017, Uber had already claimed a stunning 77% market share, with over 40 million users a month.

The 2nd phase is **DECEPTION**. This is not a nefarious concept, but rather the time when industry leaders and consumers can't believe it is true. Look at Tesla: they're a technology and battery company that happens to make cars. When they came along, they were viewed as a harmless curiosity. No one believed that an electric car could be more advanced, faster, and safer than a legacy vehicle propelled by a combustion engine. The mainstream members of the automobile industry scoffed at them, but they're not laughing now, because in recent years Tesla has consistently been rated as the safest, fastest, and most reliable vehicle on the road.

Tesla sold more automobiles than Mercedes Benz in the United States in 2018. Even as upstart companies try to adopt their model, Tesla has a three-year lead on any other electric car company. This

leads to the likelihood that the cost of a Tesla will soon be lower than that of a Toyota Camry. Today's estimates are that a base model Tesla will cost $15,500 in three years. Imagine being able to buy a fully autonomous vehicle, 100% powered by electricity, and safer than any other car ever made for that price. It's coming!! I've owned Teslas for over six years now and have yet to have a mechanical problem or the need to go to a gas station.

While we've eliminated or reduced the impact of many diseases that were common a generation ago, accidental deaths persist. Opioids are currently the top cause, but right behind them are automobile accidents, **94% of which result from human error**. Simply put, the adoption of advanced autonomous vehicles will save lives.

Some naysayers still suppose that Tesla is on the road to going out of business. To the contrary, in ten years Tesla is highly likely to be among the most valuable companies in the world. Virtually every major automobile manufacturer either produces or will soon produce an electric vehicle. There are currently over three million electric vehicles on the road worldwide, and countries including India, France, China, the United Kingdom, and Norway have instituted mandates with firm deadlines by which a certain percentage of cars sold in those markets must be electric. Cathie Wood, CEO Founder of ARK Investment Management, estimates that by 2023 there will be over 25 million electric cars sold. China alone has over 500 electric car manufacturers.

"BY 2023 THERE WILL BE **OVER 26 MILLION ELECTRIC CARS SOLD**."

CATHIE WOOD
CEO FOUNDER, ARK
INVESTMENT MANAGEMENT

The 3rd phase is **DISRUPTION**. When a tipping point is identified, companies that do not make a rapid transition are left behind or destroyed. A generation ago, people spent Friday nights patrolling the aisles at Blockbuster, waiting for the latest video hits to be returned or trying to find a hidden cinematic gem. Today they are all but out of business, replaced by streaming services like Netflix, Hulu, YouTube, and even Amazon Prime. In fact, it wasn't long ago that the CEO of Blockbuster told Wall Street analysts that Netflix wasn't on the company's radar.

Similarly, Eastman Kodak long dominated the film camera industry, to the point where they were one of the 30 largest companies in the United States and a fixture on the Dow Jones Industrial Average. Not only did the company employ over 130,000 people, but they invented the digital camera. They had the technology exclusively to themselves, but they didn't take it seriously. The board of directors feared that the digital camera would cannibalize their existing business, so they downplayed its value. Six years later, they were out of business.

The 4th phase is **DEMATERIALIZATION**, which, as you might have guessed, means that you get more value out of less "stuff." As mentioned above, a prime example of this is your cell phone. Get rid of your vinyl records (unless you're a collector), your calculator, your video recorder, paper, magazines, and other cluttering detritus because now they're all literally at your fingertips all the time (assuming you remember to get a good charge).

20 YEARS LATER, **ALL THIS FITS INTO YOUR POCKET !!**

Apple's iPhone was introduced in the summer of 2007, and it's now at least eleven iterations deep, each one substantially more advanced than the last—the overused word "revolutionary" is for once apt in this circumstance.

What did the competition say about the iPhone when it first came out?

Palm's CEO refused to acknowledge that there was any threat at all: "We've learned and struggled for a few years here figuring out how to make a decent phone . . . PC guys are not going to just figure this out. They're not going to just walk in."[6] Palm still existed in 2018, but they retained only a minuscule share of the market, having been bought and sold several times since Apple obtained dominance in that space.

If you think that Palm was the only naysayer, you're wrong. "The development of mobile phones will follow a similar path to that followed by PCs," said Nokia's Chief Strategy Officer Anssi Vanjoki. "Apple attracted a lot of attention at first, but they have remained a niche manufacturer. That will be their role in mobile phones as well."[7]

The 5th phase is **DEMONETIZATION,** which refers specifically to an exponential *decrease* in cost. Something that cost $1,000 a decade ago might now retail for one-tenth or one-twentieth of that amount. When we enter the demonetization phase of the wave, it typically completely changes the landscape of the industry, forcing CEOs to rethink their business model or go out of business.

One example of demonetization involves the efforts of leading financial services firm, The Vanguard Group, in the field of mutual funds. The late John C. (Jack) Bogle, Vanguard's founder and retired Chief Executive, created the world's first index mutual fund—now known as Vanguard 500 Index Fund—for individual investors in 1976. For his pioneering of the index concept for individual investors, Mr. Bogle was often called the "father of indexing." That innovation lowered expenses for the individual investor by a factor of ten.

In 2017, the Investment Company Institute conducted a study of all equity mutual funds offered that year. The simple average expense ratio was 1.25%. This means investors would have paid, on average, 1.25% for the purchase of any given stock mutual fund. The Vanguard S&P 500

JOHN C. (JACK) BOGLE (1929 - 2019) Courtesy The Institute for Fiduciary Standard via Wikimedia Commons

ETF, meanwhile, had an average expense ratio of .09%. That means that out-of-pocket expenses for fees were 13 times less than average. It's common sense where you would place your money, and investors by and large have figured this out—as of 2018, they have collectively placed over $5 trillion under Vanguard's guidance. To place this into context, Vanguard now has more in assets under management than JP Morgan, Merrill Lynch, and Goldman Sachs combined. It's a clear example that money talks and most rational people will vote with their pocketbook.

The demonetization example that resonates most clearly with Americans is Amazon, which has established a business model aimed at being the lowest-cost provider, demonetizing whatever industry they target. They have clearly accomplished that, but at the same time they've consistently improved the user experience through digitization and artificial intelligence. Their first market was books, which led to the creation of Kindle. Today there are over 21 million Kindles in use. Perhaps more amazingly, they currently have over 100 million Amazon Prime members who pay a small amount per year and receive free shipping for most items. You don't even need to get on the phone or computer to make an order— just speak to Alexa (Amazon's artificial intelligence platform) and your wishes are granted in record time.

All these companies integrating artificial intelligence are experiencing and proving Wright's Law, an economic model that creates an "Experience Curve." When you have an industry or company growing exponentially like Netflix, Tesla, or Amazon, production times eventually collapse, and the industry is demonetized.

The 6th phase is **DEMOCRATIZATION**, the phase in which we're well past a tipping point and into the widespread distribution and adoption of the new paradigm. There was a time when a digital camera or a smartphone was considered a luxury, reserved for the special few who could afford them. That's no longer the case. Schoolchildren today have top-of-the-line phones and tablets to keep them connected and on pace to become successful adults.

Going back to the aforementioned Amazon rainforest trip, our group visited a local village one-hundred miles or so from the nearest paved road. Just a single generation ago, those same villagers may never have felt concrete beneath their feet, let alone used a computer or camera. By the time we arrived, just about everyone there had a smartphone. In the past, their only connection to the world was the rare times they took a boat a long distance. Now everything was literally at their fingertips. They even had apps I hadn't heard of, and everyone—from the oldest senior citizen to the youngest child—had incorporated them into their lives. That's democratization. There was no consumer cell phone use prior to 1982, and today there are over a staggering five billion individual cell phone users worldwide.

"Technology is disrupting traditional industrial processes, and they're never going back," Peter Diamandis wrote. For all of this, it means it's time to adapt. It's easy to be afraid of the future and to shirk its challenges, but if you meet it on its own terms, the opportunities are endless.

Most importantly, embracing transparency will enable us all to get there faster.

TRANSPARENCY CHANGES EVERYTHING !!

CHAPTER 3 | THE DIGITAL WAVE

dig·i·tal

/'dijidl/

the branch of scientific or
engineering knowledge
that deals with the creation
and practical use of digital
or computerized devices,
methods, systems, etc.

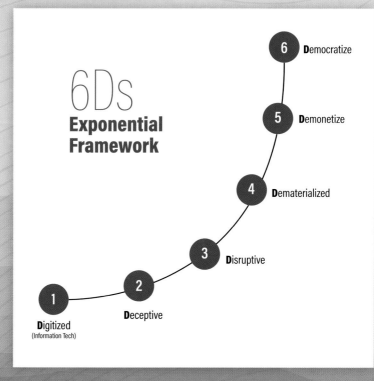

6Ds
Exponential Framework

6 **D**emocratize

5 **D**emonetize

4 **D**ematerialized

3 **D**isruptive

2 **D**eceptive

1 **D**igitized
(Information Tech)

WHY **IT MATTERS:**

- The 6Ds help show why change is occurring so rapidly in society, how a Dow company (some of the largest companies in the world), can go out of business in just five years, and what to focus on going forward.

ADVICE:

- Prepare for the new wave by continuously learning.
- Prepare for acceleration in change.

TAKE**AWAYS:**

- The first step to exponential growth is Digitization.
- Wright's Law—the Experience Curve demonstrates that exponential growth leads to a collapse in prices and Demonetization.
- There are now over two million apps with ever-shrinking barriers to entry.
- Autonomous vehicles will continue to save lives in increasing numbers.

ACTION STEPS:

- Commit the 6Ds to memory: Digitization, Deception, Disruption, Demonetization, Dematerialization, Democratization.
- Analyze and apply the 6Ds in your industry.
- Find a way to digitize what you do.

"Once a tipping point is reached,
there is no going back."

PAUL PAGNATO

TRANSPARENCY WAVE

CHAPTER 4

The Transparency Wave

Transparency has been front of mind throughout my entire life, with an interest and focus on the topic accelerating from the inception of the 2007 financial crisis. I'd worked in the financial advisory industry since 1992, but only after learning about otherwise savvy people losing their life savings at large banks did some segments of the industry's utter lack of transparency become apparent. From Bernie Madoff's Ponzi scheme, which stole over $60 billion, to the bankruptcy of the largest brokerage firm, to the collapse of the largest mortgage company, to the largest auto companies on verge of collapse, to the misdeeds of one of the largest insurance companies in the country—ALL of this could have been avoided.

They weren't looking out for their clients' best interests. They might've pretended to do so, or indicated that they were acting as "fiduciaries," without even attempting to define what the term meant. All sorts of hidden fees, costs, and kickbacks existed that prevented them from consistently achieving their clients' goals to the maximum ability.

THE THIRD WAVE OF INNOVATION: TRANSPARENCY WAVE

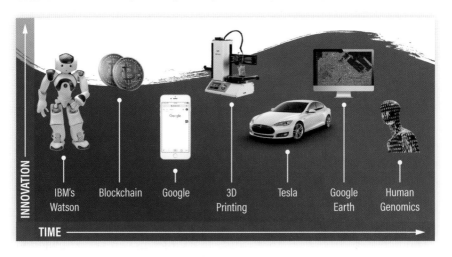

These practices were the motivating factor in becoming involved with the Institute for the Fiduciary Standard, whose goal is to build a fiduciary culture of honesty, integrity, and expertise. Along with my involvement in the Institute, a top priority became supporting the efforts of industry visionaries, like the late Jack Bogle. We share the belief that the best way to get our industry to where it needs to be is by bringing complete transparency to the front lines, whether by regulatory means, market forces, or a combination of both.

Simply put, **transparency incorporates complete openness**—the ability to express your thoughts and convey your biases while **seeking the flourishing of others**. The need for greater transparency is easy for most Americans to grasp, but incredibly hard to implement, particularly in fields where there's an imbalance of information between parties (e.g., a financial advisor and client). As technology democratizes, those barriers and imbalances are falling by the wayside.

All of this informed my development of the **6Ts of Exponential Transparency**: Transparency Standards, Terms, Total Accountability, Transparent Cost, Truth, and Trust. Throughout this book, you will learn how to develop each of these, how they build on one another, and how wildly successful companies are using them to experience exponential growth, the likes of which we've rarely seen.

I've frequently asked other thought leaders in my industry for their take on how and why we might affect more transparency across the board. One is Ric Edelman, the founder and Executive Chairman of Edelman Financial Services LLC, one of the most innovative and successful financial advisory firms in the United States. I've known Ric professionally and personally for years, and greatly respect the efforts that have led *Barron's* to name him as the top Independent Financial Advisor in the United States on multiple occasions.

Ric differs from many people in our industry in his extreme devotion to the purpose-based mission to help people with their planning needs, regardless of how much money they have to invest. His tremendous success is proof of the concept that you can "do well by doing good."

"The financial services industry guards its information and knowledge as closely as possible," Edelman said. "The only reasons these companies make any disclosures of any kind are because federal laws and regulations require them to do so. Were it not for those rules, there would not only be no information shared, there would be massive amounts of misinformation distributed to the detriment of everyone except those in power."

Nevertheless, when asked, he offered up a definition of transparency that is agnostic about the results it provides: "Transparency means full disclosure of what you're doing, what you're saying and why, along with the implications, both positive and negative, of those statements of doctrine. It means enabling the counterparty to make an informed decision that is in their best interests. Let's use Bernie Madoff as an example: It's not the fact that he was a crook; it's the fact that he didn't disclose that he was a crook."

TRANSPARENCY INCORPORATES COMPLETE OPENNESS—THE ABILITY TO EXPRESS YOUR THOUGHTS AND CONVEY YOUR BIASES **WHILE SEEKING THE FLOURISHING OF OTHERS.**

Bernie Madoff calculated client performance returns, generated client statements, took in and held clients' assets, received commissions, shared in revenues and kickbacks. All these items were legal then and are still legal today. The SEC has not addressed or changed any law prohibiting these practices. The only people benefiting from these conflicted practices are the banks, broker-dealers, and financial advisors engaged in those actions. Madoff was able to fool sophisticated people including Eliot Spitzer, the former Attorney General of New York; David Komansky, the former CEO of Merrill Lynch; actor Kevin Bacon; and owners of the New York Mets. They all allowed for these conflicted practices to occur with their capital and sadly, they paid the price.

Both of us support more transparency in our industry largely because we believe, in Ric's words, "the ordinary American consumer isn't an idiot." If you provide the rational consumer with accurate and balanced information, they can make the right choices for themselves.

Those rational decisions are more likely to be enabled as the result of enhanced technology. Today you can compare mortgage rates, insurance quotes, mutual fund fees, and health-care providers without

> "THE ONLY REASONS THESE COMPANIES MAKE ANY DISCLOSURES OF ANY KIND ARE BECAUSE **FEDERAL LAWS AND REGULATIONS REQUIRE THEM TO DO SO.**"
>
> RIC EDELMAN
> FOUNDER, EDELMAN FINANCIAL ENGINES

> ## THE ORDINARY AMERICAN CONSUMER **ISN'T AN IDIOT.**

leaving your house. As you go out for the evening, you can decide whether to use Uber or Lyft based on truly objective factors.

Furthermore, if you're on the industry side of the equation, you don't only need to look directly at your colleagues and peers to see who is doing a good job of providing service and maintaining transparency. Ric told me that he's studied Disney, Ritz Carlton, Starbucks, and Southwest Airlines for pointers. He's sent his employees to the Disney executive program and the comparable Ritz-Carlton program.

Some of this is generational in nature. Edelman explained that his 90-year-old mother grew up in an era where no one ever questioned a physician. The doctor told you to take a pill and didn't even tell you what the pill was. Many people had no idea what disease or illness they had. And no one ever dared question a doctor. "Millennials would never tolerate that," he explained. "Most Americans today would not tolerate that type of behavior. But that was commonplace in the 1930's and 40's."

This is found in the news industry, where the nightly news anchors of past generations were considered kindly old uncles and grandfathers, deliverers of unbiased news. Obviously, there were always biases, we just didn't fully recognize or acknowledge them. In today's hyper-partisan news space, we may have floated too far to the other side, where "fake news" becomes a buzzword for whatever "the other side" is saying, but it can no longer be said that we're not good consumers of the information that's provided. We have all sorts of fact-checking methodologies, so if someone is not transparent about their sources or motivations, it quickly becomes obvious, and they can be debunked and discredited.

Despite his highly nuanced and intellectual understanding of issues related to transparency, the critical importance of it to society and the exponential nature of its growth were not completely apparent to Ric until the past year or two—when the "Me Too" (#MeToo) movement arose.

Certainly, most readers should be familiar with "Me Too" by now, but in case you aren't, here's a brief synopsis of its rise and its impact. No one can question that sexual harassment and sexual assault have been common throughout history, but existing power dynamics often prevented them from being reported. For example, a female support staffer who is harassed by a male CEO might avoid reporting those incidents out of fear of losing her job. Within a religious or educational organization, a victim might avoid reporting such abuse out of fear that no one will believe them, and that they would eventually be ostracized or punished for reporting someone else's transgression—making them relive the victimhood and possibly punishing them a second time for something that was not their fault in the first place.

While the phrase "Me Too" is said to have originated in 2006,[1] it did not gain momentum until October 2017, when actress Alyssa Milano tweeted it out. By the end of the day, it had been used more than 200,000 times, and within 24 hours, it had been tweeted or posted on other social media platforms millions of times. Talk about exponential! The rise snuck up on us, and then took over the world.

As Ric said of exponentiality in general, and "Me Too" in particular: "When you look at the exponential growth curve, for the vast majority of the curve it looks like there's nothing going on. Try doubling a penny 30 times. For the first 21 doublings the increases are almost imperceptible. But then suddenly, the curve goes almost completely vertical. We're going to see that same thing in transparency. Reluctance—often resistance—to transparency at first but once it begins, it will be unstoppable, and everyone everywhere will suddenly be 100% transparent. It'll be a very long, difficult slog to get to that 'knee of the curve', but once we're there, the speed of adoption will be astonishing."

That's what's amazing about "Me Too." Not only did the numbers grow exponentially as the word spread, but so too did its scope. It expanded to people not typically expected to be subject to victimization. Actor Terry Crews, who played football at Western Michigan University, earning all-conference honors, and then in the NFL, would be the last person you'd expect to be subject to sexual harassment. He was the very definition of traditional masculinity. He could fight back if harassed, right? That's what would be expected, but it took the "Me Too" movement for him to come forward with claims that he had been groped by a Hollywood executive, and also that his father had abused his mother.

When "Me Too" created the platform and the momentum, Crews became empowered. Like many prior victims, the exponential nature of the movement allowed him to transform his shame into energy and solidarity.

"When I look at this movement . . . this is the Emancipation Proclamation," Crews stated.[2]

The exponential nature of the movement also gave rise to related splinter efforts, like "Time's Up," an effort started by celebrities to specifically but not exclusively work against sexual harassment in Hollywood. Indeed, while on the surface it was stars and public figures who made the biggest splash through "Me Too," the bottom line was it gave any person—no matter how powerless they previously perceived themselves to be—the ability to function as David to an existing power broker's Goliath.

It forced changes to existing institutions, not just in the ouster of prominent entertainers, executives, Wall Street moguls, and fixtures on Capitol Hill, but in terms of policies, expectations, and social norms. That is the power of exponential growth: it can upend the world in a matter of months or even minutes. That portends great opportunity, but it also demands greater responsibility.

If we can find a way to both encourage and harness the power of transparency, without stifling or pre-judging its growth, then the technological advances that are concurrently occurring will lead to the greatest overall flourishing.

TRANSPARENCY CHANGES EVERYTHING !!

PERSPECTIVES

CHAPTER 4 | THE TRANSPARENCY WAVE

trans·par·en·cy
/tran'sperənsē/

lack of hidden agendas and conditions,
accompanied by the availability of full information.

Transparency Changes **Everything**™

LITERACY   POVERTY   PEACE

Will this
baby live
to 142?

QUALITY   WEALTH   LONGEVITY

WHY **IT MATTERS:**

- Transparency changes everything and is far reaching in its effect, especially as it hits the exponential curve.

ADVICE:

- Wake up every day with PMA!

- Incorporate transparency into your daily life.

TAKE**AWAYS:**

- Transparency requires you to seek the flourishing of others.

- Transparency is an attitude.

- The fastest-growing and most valuable companies are the most transparent.

- Personal breakthroughs occur via transparency.

ACTION STEPS**:**

- Overcome conflict through transparency.

- Be transparent with your personal obstacles and issues.

- Create your own personal and professional standards for transparency.

"SO BE SURE WHEN YOU STEP, STEP WITH CARE AND GREAT TACT. AND REMEMBER THAT LIFE'S A GREAT BALANCING ACT. AND WILL YOU SUCCEED? YES! YOU WILL, INDEED! (98 AND 3/4 PERCENT GUARANTEED)."

DR. SEUSS

CHAPTER 5

The 6Ts of Exponential Transparency

If you look at the picture of my second-grade class, taken in 1972 at our elementary school in Jacksonville, Florida, you can't help but notice that one kid is nerdier that the rest. He wears a shirt that was probably already out of style back then (or perhaps never was in style) and thick Coke-bottle glasses.

That little geek was me.

I wear that badge proudly, though, because my nerdiness contributed to where I am today. It led to many of my greatest personal accomplishments and taught me the life lesson of not worrying about fashion as much as substance.

If my look alone didn't cement the label, my hobbies might make the picture even clearer. While other kids wanted a bicycle or sports equipment for their birthdays, I had my eyes and heart laser-focused on something much cooler—a MICROSCOPE. Even then, I was fascinated by what made things tick. I wanted a lens that helped to put issues into focus, and a microscope could provide clarity and eliminate confusion.

With that microscope, I conducted countless experiments, some of them exciting and revelatory, and others complete busts. Nevertheless, over time the failures decreased in number, even though I was tackling more advanced problems. Why? Because I'd developed systems and parameters that guided my exploration. If you provide yourself with intellectual guardrails, you can walk on the highest peaks and along the steepest drops without fear. By establishing a series of fundamentals and sets of rules, I was able to exponentially increase my chances of success.

Whether you are embarking on your first career or you've been in the business world for decades, you need to keep a constant eye on the past, present, and future. The fundamentals don't change, nor does the inherent DNA of successful businesses, but if you're not willing to adapt to changing conditions, you're going to get left behind.

Transparency is becoming a pivotal success factor for exponential growth. I've created 6Ts of Exponential Transparency to help companies optimize transparency across the board and as an easy guide for everyone to follow.

THE 6TS OF EXPONENTIAL TRANSPARENCY:

1 TRANSPARENCY STANDARDS

By creating a set of transparency standards, a company will naturally be in a place to always put the consumer's interest first. It makes transparency an essential part of the culture. At PagnatoKarp, we created True Fiduciary® standards to put the best interests of our clients first. Everything we do is built on a foundation of True Fiduciary® transparency.

2 TERMS

The terms of engagement, which function as the contract with the consumer, need to be ridiculously simple and easy to understand. The ride-share industry is a perfect example. Companies like Uber and Lyft have made the terms and experience ridiculously simple. The consumer now knows exactly what the cost of the ride is, along with the driver's profile, location, and rating. You know exactly which car will pick you up. No surprises ever.

6Ts of Exponential
TRANSPARENCY

6 TRUST

5 TRUTH

4 TRANSPARENT COST

3 TOTAL ACCOUNTABILITY

2 TERMS

1 TRANSPARENCY STANDARDS

3 TOTAL ACCOUNTABILITY

Accountability leads to quality governance. For example, Patagonia has been an exemplar of environmental responsibility and accountability. Company founder Yvon Chouinard believes that "caring for our planet is not in conflict with running a successful business." When governments are corrupt, they struggle to maintain accountability. An organization called Transparency International has created a Corruption Index, which recently noted that, on average, every week a journalist is killed in a highly corrupt country. Over the last five years, 352 journalists have been killed in countries that fall below the corruption policy index average. Accountability saves lives.

4 TRANSPARENT COST

Providing accurate and total costs is essential today. The retail industry failed to heed this truth for decades and is suffering for it now. When companies like Amazon and eBay emerged, they preyed upon this corporate vulnerability by providing transparency. Amazon Prime members receive transparent and accurate costs of the product being purchased, but they also enjoy a much better customer experience. They can enjoy same-day delivery and easy returns. The proof is in the pudding: Amazon sold five billion products last year. eBay now sells a vehicle every 90 seconds.

5 TRUTH

Truth is nothing more than the ability to openly and accurately communicate facts and messaging. The founder of The Vanguard Group, Jack Bogle, personified this notion. In our mutual service to the board of directors for The Institute for the Fiduciary Standard, I experienced Jack's passion for transparency firsthand. A champion of the individual investor, he is widely credited with helping bring increased disclosure about mutual fund costs and performance to the public. By providing total transparency on holdings, transactions, and costs, Vanguard has grown to over $5 trillion in assets under management, more than JP Morgan, Goldman Sachs, and Merrill Lynch combined.

6 TRUST

Marc Benioff, the founder of Salesforce, summed it up best: "Companies that are struggling today are struggling because of a crisis with trust."

These 6Ts of Exponential Transparency have become the fundamental guardrails and guiding light for everything that I do and will do. As you'll see in subsequent chapters, they are a critical ingredient of success, and if you apply them to every action you take, the result is maximized transparency, which leads to exponential success.

Regardless of the type of business you desire, or what stage of it you're in, there are fundamental questions that largely indicate why a business succeeds or fails.

First and foremost, a business must create value and solve a problem. That problem might reflect varying levels of complexity, but at heart it's the same process.

Founding PagnatoKarp has been one of the most fulfilling efforts of my lifetime to date. Every day I remain motivated by the ability to make a difference.

Our country is founded on capitalism, and we have a particularly successful and benevolent model of that sort. The #1 source of wealth creation occurs when an individual or partnership starts a privately-owned business and later enjoys a liquidity event. Nevertheless, of the more than 600,000 new

> FIRST AND FOREMOST, A BUSINESS MUST **CREATE VALUE AND SOLVE A PROBLEM.**

open each year, not all of them will succeed, even if their product solves a problem.

What is the primary dividing line between those that do and those that do not succeed?

It comes down to value. Increasingly, the companies that thrive and grow exponentially are the ones that adopt transparency in their organizations and create more value for their clients.

The current generation of ultra-high wealth exemplifies this. Entrepreneurs including Bill Gates, Mark Zuckerberg, Jeff Bezos, and Larry Page all provided products with widespread and transformative utility for mankind.

Bill Gates founded Microsoft and created the Word and Excel products that are now used by over 1.5 billion people. If you created something that 1.5 billion people used every week, you would also be one of the wealthiest people in the world. Jeff Bezos founded Amazon, which shipped over five billion items last year. He saves people time and money every single minute of the day.

> IT'S SIMPLE MATH. THE MORE VALUE CREATION, THE LARGER THE IMPACT, **THE MORE VALUABLE YOUR COMPANY WILL BE.**

Mark Zuckerberg has connected 1.7 billion people through Facebook. Likewise, Larry Page, cofounder of Google, helps billions of people with over two trillion Internet searches per year.

It's simple math. The more value creation, the larger the impact, and the more valuable your company will be. More value equals more impact.

WHY BUSINESSES FAIL

Before we provide the essential ingredients to success, let's examine why so many businesses don't make it.

Statistically, three in ten businesses don't survive past their first two years, and there is a consistent set of three reasons why they don't.

First and foremost, cash is king. Adequate financial backing is oxygen for a business and without it, the business will die. I've seen startups and second-generation businesses that have been around for 80 years succumb because of a lack of adequate cash flow.

As a rule of thumb, a company should have access to enough cash to sustain one to two years' worth of expenses.

The second reason businesses fail is lack of a business plan. A business plan should contain a budget, road map to an MVP (Minimum Viable Product or Service), a business model, and a clear breakthrough value proposition. *Blueprint to a Billion* by David Thomson clearly articulates what a breakthrough value proposition is and why it's so essential for every business.

A business plan need not be overwhelmingly long and should build in flexibility to account for the changing world. In fact, Peter Thiel, the founder of PayPal, recommends against creating a business plan for that reason. Still, a business plan can be valuable to ensure focus and accountability.

For example, without a properly planned budget, it will be next to impossible to forecast the cash reserves needed to sustain business operations for the next one to two years. A business plan also provides the foundation upon which a great idea can be validated with customers. This is where an MVP comes into play. Creating a minimum

viable product will enable you to test your product or service. You want to test not only the sweet spot, but on the periphery as well. In fact, sometimes the greatest success comes outside the precise zone where you expected it to occur.

The third critical mistake founders make is expanding too rapidly. In an era of exponential growth, it's hard to put the brakes on our quest to become the next Mark Zuckerberg, but growth without capital and infrastructure will crumble. The ability to change and upgrade our systems, processes, and personnel to keep up with the growth is a necessary backstop against failure.

Your founding cohort may not be the same people best equipped to run your business at $20 million of revenue or $200 million in revenue. Those levels require different skill sets and the failure to recognize that can provide a stumbling block at an unexpected time.

PURPOSE VERSUS PROFITS

In order to thrive today, a business must have a strong sense of purpose. That starts with identifying a problem and a way to fix it, and thereby unleashing value. One wonderful example is Whole Foods. Cofounder John Mackey had a mission to bring GMO transparency to the grocery store industry. He wanted to provide transparency on the quality of foods from top to bottom, even identifying instances where suppliers were not meeting ethical standards to their employees.

Mackey wrote a book titled *Conscious Capitalism,* which clearly explained the importance of balancing purpose and profits. The purpose is what drives the mission, creates the culture, and ultimately unleashes value to the client. Profits provide the resources and sustainability for furthering that purpose.

BREAKTHROUGH VALUE PROPOSITION

What is your company's "WHY?"

The answer should be to provide a Breakthrough Value Proposition (BVP) that does not exist today. For something to be considered a

BVP, there should be a 10x increase in value. Examples would be a 10x decrease in price or time savings, on a 10x increase in the quality of the user experience, transparency, and trust. It has to be that dramatic to motivate the consumer to make a change.

Thomson's *Blueprint to a Billion*, cited above, discussed the largest study to date of publicly traded companies that not only made it, but that grew exponentially. Every one of them had a BVP that distinguished them from their predecessors and competitors.

At PagnatoKarp, our company has two BVPs. The first is a set of transparency standards that distinguishes us from other wealth management firms. We call this True Fiduciary®. There is not another wealth management firm that can be called a Fiduciary Business® or

1. Embrace the Legal Fiduciary Obligation to Place Clients' Interests First	2. Deliver Comprehensive Financial Planning	3. Provide Fee-Only Advice	4. Do Not Accept Commissions
Transparency Standards **True Fiduciary®** In Your Best Interest. ■**PagnatoKarp**			5. Receive Only One Source of Revenue: Client Fees
			6. Provide Transparency on Portfolios and Investments
10. Do Not Hold Any Client Assets, Securities or Money	9. Do Not Create Products to Sell or Price Any Public Securities	8. Measure Client Performance Returns Using Independent Third Parties	7. Remain Independent from any Bank, Broker Dealer, Insurance or Custodian

advisor who can call themselves a True Fiduciary®. The exponential model of our standards strives for a 10x increase in transparency, as compared to an advisor who works for a bank, broker-dealer, or insurance company.

The second BVP is our fusion of family office services. By providing investment and portfolio management, tax services, legal and estate services, financial planning, private banking services, family counseling and a full suite of travel and lifestyle services, our value proposition aims for 10x more than a traditional wealth management firm solely focused on asset management. We call it Intelligent Wealth Management™.

MTP: MASSIVE TRANSFORMATIVE PURPOSE

- **What is the Massive Transformative Purpose (MTP) of your company or the company that you work for?**

- **What is your big idea?**

- **How are you going to unleash value for your clients or for the greater good?**

These are not simple questions to answer.

I've taken inspiration from Salim Ismail, best-selling author of *Exponential Organizations*, Chairman at OpenExO and Founding Executive Director at Singularity University. His book clearly articulates why every business should have an MTP; it's in the DNA of every exponential organization. Cathie Wood, CEO Founder of ARK Investment Management, recently described five innovation platforms that are currently being disrupted and changing the way the world works: artificial intelligence, DNA sequencing, robotics, energy storage, and blockchain technology. In each case, the companies engaged in the disruption have an MTP.

Ismail wrote that "Today, if you're not disrupting yourself, someone else is; your fate is to be either the disrupter or the disrupted. There is no middle ground."

Last year I participated in the launch of the True Fiduciary® Institute, which has as its MTP a goal to positively impact the lives of one million students through transparency and financial well-being. Approximately half of the students graduating college today are financially illiterate. Our purpose is to change that.

TRANSPARENCY AND TRUST

As the bulk of this book makes clear, transparency and trust are the cornerstones of modern society. People don't want to work for a company they don't trust, and consumers don't want to buy from a company they don't trust. Where transparency is lacking, they can't build trust and will disengage. Today every company can and should create a set of transparency standards. The ones that do will thrive, retain employees, and grow their client bases. The businesses that don't will eventually go away.

"COMPANIES THAT ARE STRUGGLING TODAY ARE STRUGGLING **BECAUSE OF A CRISIS WITH TRUST.**"

MARC BENIOFF
FOUNDER, SALESFORCE

(cc) Kenneth Yeung - www.thelettertwo.com.jpg

EXPERIMENTATION

As a child, I was fascinated by the marine environment. I wanted to scuba dive and eventually become a marine biologist. I idolized Jacques Cousteau—an explorer, inventor, conservationist, filmmaker, and oceanographer. He invented the Aqua Lung, the forerunner of modern-day regulators and scuba tanks.

My fascination with the ocean and Jacques Cousteau influenced my decision to attend Florida Atlantic University, which has a very strong marine biology program. Despite those intentions, like many young students, I eventually changed majors, determining that microbiology was my true path.

After college, I spent five years as a microbiologist working in the fields of electro-microbiology and colorimetry for McDonnell Douglas. The projects I worked on were linked to NASA contracts, and specifically to NASA's need for a black box to place on the Apollo spaceships to detect life in outer space. While microbiology was not my long-term career path, those five formative years taught me the principles and value of experimentation.

At that job I ran daily experiments, most of which were expected to fail. While they didn't necessarily attain our end goal, those "failures" nevertheless provided additional data. Each data point was a clue to solving the final puzzle. As my friend Salim Ismail wrote, "The biggest risk is not taking any risk."

"THE BIGGEST RISK IS
NOT TAKING ANY RISK."

SALIM ISMAIL
FOUNDER, OPENEXO
AND EXO WORKS

When I left McDonnell Douglas and entered the business world, those lessons stayed with me. It didn't matter if the experiment was related to portfolio management, financial planning, taxes, marketing, or relationship management, all the same

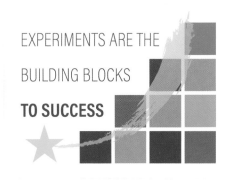

EXPERIMENTS ARE THE BUILDING BLOCKS **TO SUCCESS**

fundamentals applied—experiment, collect the data, and on the far side, be one step closer to success.

Today, all team members at PagnatoKarp are not just encouraged but **expected** to experiment. We recognize that most experiments are going to fail, but that's not a catastrophe—it's a building block.

Here's how we think about it: If there are eight areas of the business and each area has five experiments per quarter, we have 40 experiments underway. If only two to three of those 40 experiments work, we will be able to increase the value proposition to our clients every quarter.

Our company's growth is premised upon the acceptance of occasional failure. My favorite quote is one often attributed to poet Edgar A. Guest, who wrote in 1921 that "Success is failure turned inside out." Many successful companies employ the term "fail fast." As Salim Ismail wrote in the international best-seller Exponential Organizations, "When failure is not an option, you end up with safe, incremental innovation, with no radical breakthroughs or disruptive innovations." Experimentation creates data, and the data provides the clues to success.

EXECUTION

Another difference between the top companies in a given industry and their less-successful peers is the ability to execute.

At PagnatoKarp, we maintain an open-door policy—we quite literally invite our peers to our offices. We have never turned down another advisor's request to meet team members, learn our best practices, or visit our offices. The attitude we employ is, "Always seek the flourishing of others." Our ultimate goal is to help other advisors become a True Fiduciary®, create a true family office, and improve the overall experience for clients.

Over the last 27 years, I've witnessed time and time again that not many organizations have the ability to execute like we do. Proper execution is hard. It requires laser focus bordering on obsession and complete trust in the team. Execution requires sacrifices and a relentless pursuit of the task at hand. Not everyone is willing to pay the price and make the sacrifices to consistently execute at a very high level.

OUTSOURCE

Every organization is occasionally faced with the question of whether a specific task should be outsourced or handled internally.

My advice: whenever possible, outsource.

The fastest-growing companies in the world all follow this model. Because of the exponential nature of our times, much of what we do every day can be tasked to others in a seamless fashion.

When this issue arises, ask yourself if the skill set needed for the task is uniquely within the company's walls. If the answer is "no," do everything possible to outsource. Statistically, it's almost always the case that there will be someone better at executing the work—superior quality at a better price and with a time savings to you.

We used to put together client performance reports internally. We felt that no one else could possibly understand our clients as well as we do, so there was no way they could customize the reports to our standards. Eventually we were forced to question those assumptions.

It turns out we were totally wrong.

We found a company called Addepar (developed by the original owners of PayPal) that focuses exclusively on financial reporting for ultra-high-net-worth individuals. They invested hundreds of millions of dollars in assembling their team and their technology and they handle this better than anyone, so outsourcing this function increased value to our clients, increased transparency, enhanced the satisfaction of our team members, and created efficiency at great scale. Everyone won.

The "gig" economy now employs more than one-third (36%) of the population. The number of individuals who can work for themselves, in their desired field, from their desired location, shows no signs of abating. That provides even greater opportunities for companies to outsource. The Transparency Wave is fostering open software platforms, transparent employee compensation, and a higher level of accountability. It's a "perfect storm" that benefits us all.

MENTORS

In each professional endeavor I've taken seriously—as a scientist, then financial advisor, professional bass fisherman, and now entrepreneur—I've relied heavily on expert mentors. Their contributions are the primary reasons behind my professional and personal growth.

Growing up, my parents always placed an emphasis on education, family, and team sports, and they pushed me to become the first person in our family to earn a college degree. Because they hadn't received higher educations, there were certain things they couldn't help with in school, but rather than seeing that as an albatross around, I saw value in the need to seek outside help. This pattern has continued since childhood.

It started with teachers and coaches when realizing the value of expert advice and finding that people actually want to help. At McDonnell Douglas, experienced scientists all lent their time to my professional development.

When joining Merrill Lynch, I was financially illiterate and quickly had to learn the basics of portfolio management, financial planning, relationship management, and business development. Some of the top advisors and managers in the country made time to speak with me, and it just took a simple phone call.

While competing in professional bass fishing tournaments, I leaned upon the wisdom and experience of more seasoned competitors who had already put in their 10,000 hours. Once again, it shortened the learning curve.

Even when launching and growing my wealth management business for CEO Founders, you'd figure that the big dogs would want to protect their trade secrets and their wisdom. Not at all. So many experts helped me achieve my success, and I am thankful to each of them.

We are only as good as the people around us. It is always among my top priorities not only to seek the best mentors possible, but also to pay their kindness forward. As your professional career advances and shifts, you will need different mentors. I have never been turned down when asking someone to be a mentor, and don't believe you will be, either.

PMA!!

In our day-to-day lives, we cannot control the weather, the people around us, traffic, or the markets. The economy is out of our hands. So are the taxes we pay, the laws that regulate us, and thousands of other things that affect us every day.

There is one thing we can consistently control, though.

The one thing we can control is our attitude.

We have a choice when we wake up each day to greet the world with a PMA (Positive Mental Attitude) or a negative mental attitude. The choice is obvious. Positivity connects to positivity. Negativity connects to negativity. People want to be around positive people. Positivity is contagious. If you visualize success and embrace positive thoughts, you will experience the confidence to overcome any obstacles on the road to success.

Remember, "the first negative thought is a thought to failure."

When a negative thought enters your mind, acknowledge the thought and discard it. This is the one differentiator you will always have between you and the majority of your peers. This is also one of the greatest opportunities to make a difference to others. If you can lift someone's spirits when they're down, help someone break through a ceiling of complexity, or overcome a personal struggle, the value will come back to you tenfold. I truly believe the people around me—my family members, team members, friends, clients, and mentors—enjoy being with me because of my PMA. The goal is to consistently make a difference to all of them because of PMA, and you can do the same for the people in your orbit.

TRANSPARENCY CHANGES EVERYTHING !!

THERE IS
ONE THING
WE CAN
CONSISTENLY
CONTROL:
OUR ATTITUDE.

CHAPTER 5 | THE 6TS OF EXPONENTIAL TRANSPARENCY

ex·po·nen·tial

/ekspəˈnen(t)SH(ə)l/

growth whose rate becomes ever more rapid in proportion to the growing total number or size.

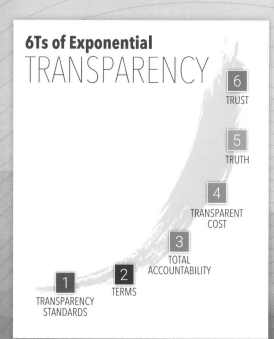

6Ts of Exponential
TRANSPARENCY

6 TRUST

5 TRUTH

4 TRANSPARENT COST

3 TOTAL ACCOUNTABILITY

2 TERMS

1 TRANSPARENCY STANDARDS

SUCCESS IS FAILURE TURNED INSIDE OUT.

WHY **IT MATTERS:**

- Wealth creation occurs through entrepreneurship. Following the ten key attributes of a successful business will increase the likelihood of success.

- Understanding the 6Ts of Exponential Transparency will set you apart from your competition.

ADVICE:

- Experiment—the more experiments, the faster the failure and the quicker the success. Experiments force change and change fuels growth.

- Complacency is a habit. The definition of insanity is doing the same thing over and over and expecting a different result.

- The one thing we can control every day is our attitude.

TAKE**AWAYS:**

- Companies creating abundance of value are the ones growing exponentially.

- Transparency and trust are the cornerstones of modern society.

ACTION STEPS**:**

- Create a set of transparency standards and follow the 6Ts of Exponential Transparency.

- Ignite your company's culture, instill trust with clients, and enable the business to break through ceilings of complexity.

"Digital privacy
violations and data
breaches greatly
threaten our Democracy."

TIM COOK

CHAPTER 6

The Defining Issue
Going Forward

Our current information age provides great opportunities for transparency to flourish and to benefit society, but that opportunity comes with a caveat—as we generate more information, and the means of distribution become increasingly democratized, institutions will work harder to retain power imbalances, and the removal of gatekeepers may have unintended consequences. In talks that I deliver around the world, in everyday business meetings, and in informal gatherings, the topic that I'm asked about most frequently is the **intersection of transparency and personal privacy**. Of course, we are all very much justified to be concerned about digital transparency. At the same time, we need to move beyond pure fear to understand how, when, and why the proper disclosure can lead to overall personal and societal benefits.

This is exceptionally evident in the media sphere. Think back to 30 or 40 years ago, when most of us got a daily newspaper, tied to our geographic location, and had three major networks to choose from in receiving our evening news. Now, many then-powerful newspapers are either gone or in freefall, and most of us have hundreds of television channels to choose from, plus literally millions of Internet sites to peruse. Anyone can become a citizen-journalist from the comfort of home, simply by creating a rudimentary website. If that requires too much effort, a Twitter, Instagram, or Facebook feed may have the same impact. By distributing simple information through those means, we have a previously unheard-of ability to affect the discourse.

Nevertheless, separating the wheat from the chaff can be tough in an increasingly complicated world. As Dr. David Bray, Executive Director of the People-Centered Internet, said, "For most of our human history, up until the last 3,000 years or so, we ran into 80 people in an entire lifespan. We averaged about 80 people who were mostly immediate family members. And now we're in this period of civilization where we run into at least 80 people daily. The change is that these are not our immediate family members—and we

> "FOR MOST OF OUR HUMAN HISTORY, UP UNTIL THE LAST 3,000 YEARS OR SO, **WE RAN INTO 80 PEOPLE IN AN ENTIRE LIFESPAN.**"
>
> DR. DAVID BRAY
> EXECUTIVE DIRECTOR,
> THE PEOPLE-CENTERED INTERNET

encounter different views or different perspectives, their different ways of seeing the world. The trouble, though, is **our brain still wants to oversimplify things, saying you're either with us or you're not, when in fact it might actually be more complicated**."

It's not that the prior methods were foolproof. As my friend Wyatt Andrews, a former National Correspondent for CBS News and now a professor in the Department of Media Studies at the University of Virginia, told me, historically American news media functioned as "an arm of the advertising industry." Certainly, that led to biases and occasional skewing of news stories. Nevertheless, just because those venues have been deposed, replaced, or supplemented does not mean that those incentives have been erased. Today's media still depends on "clicks" and "views" as a source of revenue.

Social media has, of course, had the greatest impact on the media revolution, giving every person a voice and allowing that voice to be spread exponentially across the world in a matter of seconds. As Andrews said, in practice it also tended to allow "nonsense . . . to outweigh facts." The result is that **"fake news" has become a weaponized buzzword**, allowing anyone who doesn't like a particular viewpoint or statement to belittle someone else's position on the premise that it has been developed with a particular end in mind, regardless of the underlying facts.

Andrews continued, "the evidence is that a growing number of people live in their own echo chambers because they only consume news on Facebook where they get it for free. The Facebook algorithm is wired and programmed to reward strong reaction from you. So, Facebook is measuring your likes, your shares, and loves it when you comment and repost other things. And then the algorithm figures out what you are most interested in and what draws the most emotional reaction from you. When they invented this algorithm, the presumption—think about the Arab Spring—was that this was a great way to spread the word of democracy and use that as a galvanizing force on social media to topple the dictators in Tunisia and Egypt and begin to threaten the dictator in Syria."

"The problem is that the managers of Facebook underestimated the emotional reaction you can get from hate, grievance and senses of nationalism," continued Andrews, "and that's the problem. That's why we had so much fake news impacting our election in 2016. The Facebooks of the world, well, Facebook in particular and certainly Twitter, were very slow to recognize that the same algorithmic science that has you react emotionally to a puppy also has you react emotionally to a provocative point of view. And then if you accept that, that's where nonsense began to outweigh facts on Facebook in 2016."

Even if news acquisition has become less difficult, Dr. David Bray said, "Information that is being shared by and large probably won't be repeated with complete fidelity by the news media or by the social grapevine. So, when you share information online, recognize that it may be distorted, taken out of context, or lost in the noise, often in an effort to polarize people." Who is a trusted actor? Does the fact that they are seeking to profit from their news distribution efforts impact our view of them? Does one transgression by a dissemination source undermine their overall message or their entire body of work?

These are critical questions to answer because literally the fate of the world depends on them. As we saw with the 2016 elections, there exists the possibility that determined nefarious actors can change the overall discourse or at the very least muddy the waters. If unsourced and unsubstantiated assertions have every bit as much weight and impact as diligently researched statements and conclusions, then enhanced transparency means very little.

The Facebook algorithm in and of itself is not evil. It only gives you what it perceives you to want and need. For example, if your browsing history suggests that you would benefit from a sale at Best Buy, then when such a sale occurs, it's going to get you that information promptly (assuming it is incentivized to do so, financially or otherwise), either directly or subliminally. If you are someone who responds enthusiastically to political vitriol and conspiracies, then you can likely expect to find more of that in your feed. So, while Facebook may give you more access to a wider array of information, the way that information is curated and presented will have an impact on how you digest it.

Somewhat ironically, the algorithm that provides the potential for massive transparency is not itself transparent. We don't know how it ranks items, how it transmits information, or how often it changes. We may think we understand how our news feed is being generated, yet there are sources beyond our comprehension that may influence what we see and learn. Wyatt Andrews recognizes that to be the case, and while we can never act with 100% certainty, he said that it's critical to "game" the system as much as possible.

"One of the things I teach my students out loud is train your algorithms," Andrews said. "If everything is being ranked online by algorithms, much of it is based on popularity as opposed to civic importance. I have to tell these students, 'Train your algorithm to give you different, adverse points of view.' That will help you get exposed to the diversity that you need."

"WHEN YOU SHARE INFORMATION ONLINE, RECOGNIZE THAT IT MAY BE DISTORTED, TAKEN OUT OF CONTEXT, OR LOST IN THE NOISE, **OFTEN TIMES IN AN EFFORT TO POLARIZE PEOPLE**."

DR. DAVID BRAY, PCI EXECUTIVE DIRECTOR

Not all institutions or industries make their methodologies as opaque as Facebook. Indeed, while we wouldn't expect the military to divulge their upcoming plans, and classified information is classified for a reason, in other venues the greater good (along with the individual good) is made by opening key information to outsiders.

Take, for example, open-source software, in which initial developers who own the intellectual property for source code opened it up to the public, allowing others to both examine and change its "electronic DNA." On first impression, it sounds like they'd be giving up their competitive advantage allowing others to grasp the "secret sauce" that has made them unique thought leaders in their fields. In some cases that might be true but think of it from a different perspective—by exposing the guts of their system to a broader array of perspectives and talents, they're actually working to benefit from others and to evolve the field of computing. It took a while in the early days for developers and companies to buy into this concept—changing "users" to "codevelopers"—but in addition to moving the software forward technologically, it also tends to result in increased use. Thus, promoting openness leads to the flourishing of others, which in turn leads to the furtherance of one's own goals.

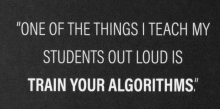

"ONE OF THE THINGS I TEACH MY STUDENTS OUT LOUD IS **TRAIN YOUR ALGORITHMS**."

WYATT ANDREWS
PROFESSOR, MEDIA STUDIES AT
UNIVERSITY OF VIRGINIA

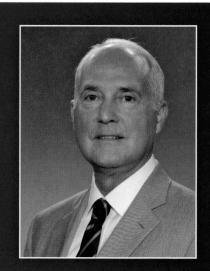

Corporate giants like Microsoft—some of whom were slow to come around—have eventually recognized the two-way power of disaggregating the development process.

"We have any number of master and PhD students, so being visible, being a thought leader, not only helps drive the field in areas of interest to us, it also gives us credibility when we want to bring in the very best people in the field," Microsoft's Chief Technology Officer, Raghu Ramakrishnan, said in early 2018.[1]

"VINT CERF AND I AGREE 100% THAT THE INTERNET IS AN ONGOING EXPERIMENT. I THINK WHAT WE'RE JUST TRYING TO DO IS ENCOURAGE ONE MORE OF THOSE EXPERIMENTS THAT AIMS TO DELIVER A **MORE BENEVOLENT FUTURE FOR US ALL.**"

DR. DAVID BRAY, PCI EXECUTIVE DIRECTOR

In December 2018, Microsoft, which had long resisted open source, "doubled down" on their open source efforts, moving away from their proprietary products and toward more collaborative efforts. The company "essentially agreed to grant a royalty-free and unrestricted license to its entire patent portfolio"[2] to all members of the Open Invention Network (OIN).

This is hardly an insubstantial change. **The 60,000 patents in question produced a whopping $3.4 billion on those patents in the single year** of 2014, with a billion of that coming from a single customer.[3] Thus, by no means can we assume that a company so powerful, so thoughtful, and so historically significant in its field undertook this decision lightly. They're reducing their litigation budget and efforts, they're enhancing their credibility, reconciling with perceived "enemies" (i.e., competitors), and giving both customers and developers a meaningful suite of choices. This is transparency in practice.

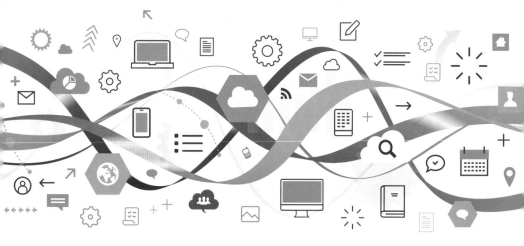

"**We see open source as central to our company mission and what our customers are trying to achieve**," the company's chief intellectual property counsel, Erich Andersen, said. "We believe the protection OIN offers the open-source community helps increase global contributions to and adoption of open-source technologies. We are honored to stand with OIN as an active participant in its program to protect against patent aggression in core Linux and other important open-source software technologies."[4]

If Microsoft, a company that historically has zealously guarded its intellectual property on its way to near-dominance of an industry, can take stock of itself and its industry and realize that transparency is often better than closely held secrets, what ethos does that convey to the rest of the world?

It is more of a milestone than you might think, because it tells people across industries and across borders that there is something to be gained from openness and by allowing others to see "how the sausage is made." Rather than fearing transparency, we can view it as a tool, even as a competitive advantage, if you're still thinking in those sorts of binary terms.

Other tech giants have also seen the benefits of integrating transparency into their everyday business practices. Apple, for example, has endeavored to create more transparency in the business relationship between the consumer and the digital company utilizing their data. **The companies that succeed will be the ones that maximize and optimize such transparency**. "The real thing is when I am going to use a service,

I should be provided clear transparency on what will happen with my data," said my good friend and colleague Manu Sharma, founder and CEO of Labelbox, a leading artificial intelligence company. "It's amazing that most companies don't provide that. I think Apple has done a pretty good job, but even so, there's a lot more work to do over time."

He's living up to those standards at Labelbox: "**We do not store all of the data in the cloud and we do not have rights to share that data or even use it for internal purposes**. Basically, the data comes to Labelbox, it goes into the server, and that's it. There are no other third-party services we tap into or things like that. However, there is the other element of aggregated anonymous data, which are like metrics being tracked, such as when or how often you click a certain button or things that we use, and we share with a variety of different services because we are already for that. And yes, we've been working very hard to further strengthen this, and I think we are on the correct path. While we use just one server, we also allow customers to keep the data in their own servers because they never have to move it to us. I think all these things help, but at the same time, they are not the solution yet because breaches will happen."

Tim Cook delivered a passionate commencement speech to Stanford University's class of 2019, in which he conveyed that digital privacy violations and data breaches greatly threaten our democracy. Although Cook did not call out any specific companies by name, the fact that the speech took place in Silicon Valley and mentioned data breaches

> "THE REAL THING IS WHEN I AM GOING TO USE A SERVICE, I SHOULD BE PROVIDED CLEAR **TRANSPARENCY ON WHAT WILL HAPPEN WITH MY DATA.**"
>
> MANU SHARMA
> CEO FOUNDER,
> LABELBOX

and privacy violations led many listeners to infer that he was calling out some of the tech giants. He also made reference to disgraced genetic testing startup Theranos.

"Lately it seems this industry is becoming better known for a less noble innovation—the belief you can claim credit without accepting responsibility," Cook said. "We see it every day now with every data breach, every privacy violation, every blind eye turned to hate speech, **fake news poisoning our national conversation**, the false miracles in exchange for a single drop of your blood." Apple's easily accessible transparency standards show the company's commitment to accepting responsibility going forward.

Any company, organization or individual that wants to be at the leading edge of this societal transformation—and reap those benefits—can likewise adopt similar standards. It's something we've actively been working on every day in our business. The key is to tailor it to your specific architecture. While Apple may have five categories in their standards, another entity could have ten or more. The key is to make them transparent, above-board, and comprehensive.

"One of the challenges with standards is that they have to work with everyone," Sharma said. "Starting with someone at a higher level aligns everyone together, and then companies and industries can go deeper into the nuances of what that really means for them."

At the same time, forward-thinking regulators may not be able to keep up with the pace of technological advances, but they can nevertheless provide the architecture and incentives under which transparency will thrive. The European Union (EU) has taken the lead in providing transparent leadership on the governance of personal digital data. **The EU created a set of standards called the General Data Protection Regulation (GDPR)**, which makes clear that harvested personal data shall not be made public without the explicit, informed consent of the individual. Furthermore, that individual may revoke their consent at any time.

The **GDPR** endeavors to answer the following questions about our personal digital data:

- **Who owns the data?**
- **What data is being collected?**
- **How long will the data be stored?**
- **How shall an individual be notified in case of a breach?**
- **How shall data collection policies be transmitted to the consumer?**
- **What can the data be used for?**
- **How can the owner gain access?**
- **How can the owner delete data?**
- **How and when can the data be transferred?**

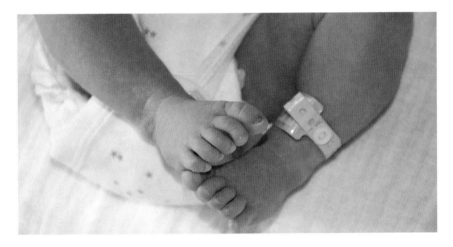

While the federal government of the United States has not yet adopted a comprehensive policy like the EU's, we can see the spirit of it in some state-level developments. An example is the transparency of genetic testing of newborn babies. While there is no federal law requiring that newborn babies be screened for genetic problems, all fifty states and the District of Columbia have implemented such requirements.

According to WebMD, the five most frequently implemented screening measures for newborns include:

1. **Heart tests**, which assess issues that currently impact **over a million** births worldwide per year;

2. Tests for **neural tube defects** like spina bifida, which impact over **324,000** births worldwide annually;

3. Blood tests that identify issues like **sickle cell anemia**, which currently impacts over **300,000** newborns annually;

4. A test for **Down syndrome**, which affects over **200,000** newborns per year; and

5. Tests for **enzyme disorders**, which impact an estimated **177,000** newborns annually.

The **state of California has collected newborns' DNA since** 1983 through a public health program called Newborn Screening (NBS). Under the NBS guidelines, all parents are informed of their right to request that their child's sample be destroyed, but the state does not confirm that parents get that information before storing or selling the child's DNA. The California Department of Public Health reported that from 2015–2017 alone, the NBS protocols diagnosed 2,498 babies with a "serious congenital heart disorder that, if left untreated, could have caused irreparable harm or death."

While we are rightfully concerned about who ends up with our genetic information, fearing that it might be used for discriminatory purposes, we are also concerned about where our financial data goes. Therefore, the information held by financial institutions is very highly regulated. In 1978, Congress passed the Right to Financial Privacy Act (RFPA), which requires individuals to be provided with notice and an opportunity to object before a financial institution can disclose their personal financial information to the government. The law also strictly precludes employees of financial institutions from maintaining or storing clients' personal financial information in certain manners.

Ultimately, it will take some combination of private sector leadership and public sector oversight to come closest to the perfect balance of privacy and transparency, but am confident that the building blocks are there, along with examples of how transparency can rule the world. It will take leaders across all industries and across the world to make this happen, but individuals have the power to keep the ball rolling by adopting these standards in their own lives and accepting nothing less from anyone with whom they transact.

TRANSPARENCY CHANGES EVERYTHING !!

CHAPTER 6 | THE DEFINING ISSUE
GOING FORWARD

pri·va·cy

/ˈprīvəsē/

the right to be free from secret
surveillance and to determine whether,
when, how, and to whom, one's
personal or organizational
information is to be revealed.

WHY **IT MATTERS:**

- The algorithms processing our data impact the information delivered to us and nearly every decision we make.
- Information shared online may be distorted, taken out of context, or lost in the noise.

ADVICE:

- Be aware of fake news—consider the accuracy and motivations of the news source.
- Algorithm transparency standards are needed to keep pace with technology changes.

TAKE**AWAYS:**

- People, corporations, and regulators all need to work together to provide balance between privacy and transparency.
- The privacy of human data is broad-based across many industries, ranging from social media to heath care to financial.
- Today's media requires clicks and views as a source of revenue.
- The companies providing transparency on the use of our personal data will flourish.

ACTION STEPS**:**

- Train your algorithms to give you different, adverse points of view to expose you to diversity.
- Request and understand the privacy practices of companies holding your personal data.

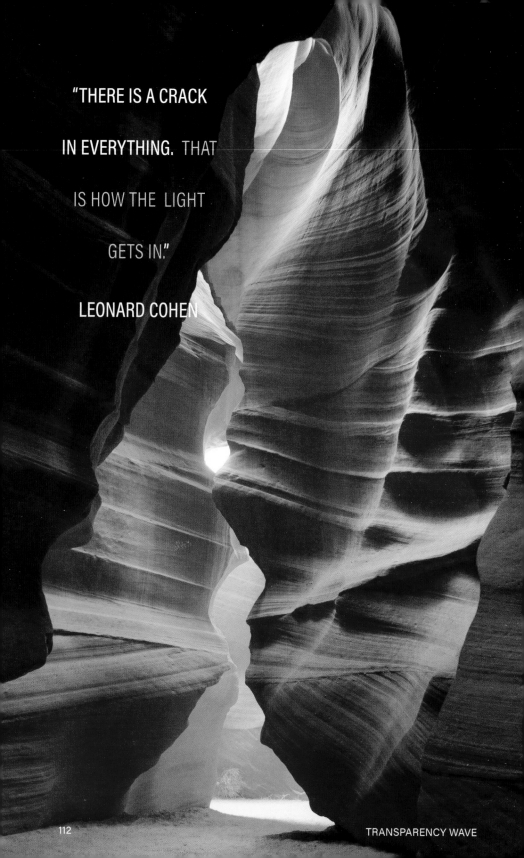

"THERE IS A CRACK

IN EVERYTHING. THAT

IS HOW THE LIGHT

GETS IN."

LEONARD COHEN

TRANSPARENCY WAVE

CHAPTER 7

Perceptions

Transparency is not always a two-way street, nor is projected or presumed transparency always what it claims to be. As discussed later, the field of genomics is moving at a truly exponential pace. Some of the developments put Moore's Law to shame—it's not a matter of doubling every few years, but rather of growth measured by factors of 10x, 20x, or 100x. We can gather much more information, at a substantially faster pace and lower cost, than ever before. Yet not everyone who enters the fray is a good actor.

Theranos, a company founded by Stanford student Elizabeth Holmes, claimed to conduct blood tests for a wide variety of conditions and diseases with only microscopic amounts of blood. If proven, this would completely disrupt the industry and provide consumers with vastly more information at their fingertips (no pun intended), at a far lower cost than ever before, with increased convenience and without an unnecessary middleman or gatekeeper.

At its peak, Theranos was valued at approximately $10 billion. Holmes became a celebrity, making rounds through the media and Silicon Valley investors, touting the revolutionary nature of their product. Even the Food and Drug Administration, normally a careful source of scientific scrutiny, was fooled by the company's claims and authorized Theranos products for certain medical purposes.

Oddly enough, the undoing of Theranos came not through technological failures or investor doubts, but rather through the efforts of legacy media presuming it to be a dying enterprise. This was specifically through the reporting of The Wall Street Journal. A positive introduction to the company was given by The Wall Street Journal a few years earlier, but once investigative reporter John Carreyrou started investigating the claims made by Holmes, things started to unravel. It wasn't an easy tale to undo, especially when many sophisticated investors were riding the company's wave enthusiastically—they may have claimed that they weren't duped, but a billion dollars in investor capital from the likes of Rupert Murdoch, Carlos Slim, and the DeVos family speaks to the scale of this deception. Simply put, there had been inadequate due diligence and lots of opaque answers. What if Theranos had created a set of transparency standards? What if they had implemented the 6Ts of Exponential Transparency: Transparency Standards, Terms, Total Accountability, Transparent Costs, Truth, and Trust? The outcome would have saved people's careers and billions of investor dollars.

The question for most of us becomes, "How do we ascertain the best possible information?"

It's not easy. The best competitive advantage—or at least the perceived best competitive advantage—often lies in an imbalance of information. It's even better if a company can tout its transparency while keeping that one-sided. For example, I love my Tesla and think that Elon Musk is a visionary genius. The car is more than a vehicle—it is an information center, a high-powered computer, and an iterative machine all in one. It is constantly taking in information that provides a net positive user experience. The way that it assesses and adjusts makes things safer. At the same time, everything that the driver does behind the wheel is captured. In the case of a liability issue, Tesla can dissect a wealth of data points and explain what happened. Tesla already has stored the driving patterns of ten billion miles.

> THE QUESTION FOR MOST OF US BECOMES, **"HOW DO WE ASCERTAIN THE BEST POSSIBLE INFORMATION?"**

With that additional convenience, there comes a great deal of concern. What if Tesla refuses to share that information? What if someone has incriminating evidence against the company or one of its engineers or executives? If they will only disclose such information under a subpoena or some other means of force, what does that mean? Is one-way transparency really transparent, or is it more like the one-way mirror in a police examination room, where one party sees and hears what the other says and does, but not vice versa?

Think of just about any disruptive company and these same issues exist, especially where disruption becomes an all-encompassing guiding principle rather than a means to specific ends. Netflix provides you with information with extraordinary speed and breadth, unlike anything Blockbuster could have conceived of, but they are surely gathering information about you—what types of titles you click, how long you view them, at what time or times of day, and on what sorts of devices.

Is this harmless? Maybe. It could even be beneficial if they target you with ads and programming of which you would otherwise not be aware. Now you'll know about a product that's better than the one you intended to buy, and it'll be delivered to you the next day for a price far lower than you could find in your local brick-and-mortar stores. That's great, but what if the targeted content is political, ethical, or psychological?

Without opining on the ethics of Netflix and its decision-makers, they have a **tremendous amount of power in their hands**. Without trying to sound like something out of a superhero comic book, they have the potential to use it for good, evil, or a combination of the two.

Do you think that's a bit farfetched? Think about how social media, which most of us would agree has many distinct and unprecedented benefits, can be utilized for underhanded ends. Indeed, there is virtual consensus that the 2016 presidential election (and possibly elections before and since then) were influenced by interlopers on social media. They may have been from a foreign country or they may have been domestic operatives, but even if they didn't exist, who is to say that the Facebook algorithm isn't rewarding you with a dopamine blast every time you see a particularly controversial or pointed post?

Again, somewhere on the far side of convenience lies creepiness.

Who could have imagined the "vision of a worldwide network of connected computers would morph 45 years later into a surveillance system that collects personal information or a propaganda machine that could sway elections," reported AP News.[1]

"We had no idea [the Internet] would turn into a global and public infrastructure," said Vint Cerf, Google's Chief Internet Evangelist, when asked about codeveloping the Internet. "We were just trying to get it to work. But now that it's in the hands of the general public, there are people who... want it to work in a way that obviously does harm, or benefits themselves, or disrupts the political system. We are going to have to deal with that."[2]

If there are forces, companies, and individuals who depend on our ignorance to continue to prosper, the best antidote and medicine is to demand more openness by helping them realize that their success is more closely tied to the flourishing of others. That's exponential transparency.

TRANSPARENCY CHANGES EVERYTHING !!

"WE HAD NO IDEA THAT THE INTERNET WOULD TURN INTO A **GLOBAL AND PUBLIC INFRASTRUCTURE**."

VINT CERF
CO-FATHER OF THE INTERNET

PERSPECTIVES

CHAPTER 7 I PERCEPTIONS

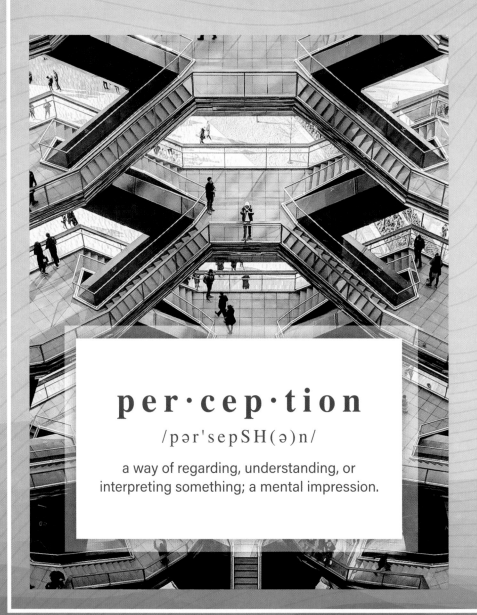

per·cep·tion
/pər'sepSH(ə)n/

a way of regarding, understanding, or
interpreting something; a mental impression.

TRANSPARENCY WAVE

WHY **IT MATTERS:**

- Transparency is not always a two-way street. Perceived competitive advantage often lies in an imbalance of information.

ADVICE:

- Transparency is the epicenter of wealth creation.

- Demand transparency when conducting due diligence.

TAKE**AWAYS:**

- Never make an investment that lacks complete transparency.

- Never invest in a black box.

- Meaningful transparency would have prevented catastrophic losses like those engineered by Bernie Madoff and Theranos.

ACTION STEPS**:**

- Implement the 6Ts of Exponential Transparency.

- Create your own set of transparency standards.

- Incorporate transparency into your investment discipline.

"Apple Computer's greatest innovation was the creation of apps."

Steve Wozniak

CHAPTER 8

Generational Shift

So, in an era when "fake news" and "deep state" and "trade secrets" have become weaponized, where do we look for a push in the right direction, away from buzzwords and toward clarity?

Even though Millennials are often criticized by the older members of society for their habits, preferences, and goals, I've observed that, as a generation, they are on the forefront of the battle for practical transparency. They demand it and expect it.

When did this hit home for me?

It happened when noticing that my 20-something children were not using cash or checks or other "old" means of payments to settle debts and minor obligations to their friends. Instead, they were reliant on more technologically advanced methodologies, and the latest and most popular apps all used transparency as their driving force.

Indeed, the 6Ts of Exponential Transparency are transforming "pay me back later" into a thing of the past.

For years, if a group of friends wanted to split a restaurant tab and everyone at the table only carried big bills, the likely result was a series of verbal IOUs. Then the person who'd paid the bill would have to wait for their friends to either pick up the next tab, send cash, or write a check, which involved finding a stamp, envelope, and a mailbox, plus a visit to the bank by the recipient and a waiting period for the check to clear. Even under the most streamlined model, this was woefully inefficient and inevitably led to frustration.

Last year my wife, normally the calmest and most even-keeled person I know, called me in a panic. The person who'd been cleaning our house for the prior five years informed her that she would no longer accept checks as payment.

My wife then asked me if I've ever heard of Venmo.

She couldn't see it across the phone line, but I was grinning ear to ear and knew where this was headed. After a brief fifteen-minute tutorial on Venmo, my wife was up and running and no longer concerned. Later that week, she told me how much she loved the app and had also utilized it to effortlessly transfer funds to one of our children. In one week, she'd gone from having to write a check and manually balance the checkbook to a digital experience that eliminated those steps and greatly simplified her life. This is a wonderful example of **turning a negative into a positive**. Day by day, human by human, we are all making this transition to digital services.

The following week, my wife and I went to dinner with some of our best friends. The husband runs one of the largest wealth management firms in the country. His wife was upset that the bank she'd used for the last decade had closed the drive-through teller station. For years she'd made it a habit to go with her dog, make a deposit, and the dog would receive a nice treat. Now she had to sit through a presentation from the bank representative on how to make a deposit via an ATM machine. Not only was it complicated and uncertain, but the dog got no treat! That left her upset.

PAYMENTS TO EACH OTHER CAN NOW BE **IMMEDIATE, PRECISE, AND SAFE.**

My wife, who'd effectively been in her shoes just a few days earlier, now had wonderful news to share about her positive experiences with Venmo. Our friend's husband shared his positive experiences with PayPal. I regaled her with the advantages I'd found by using Square. Our 3 positives greatly outweighed her perceived sense of loss. By the end of the evening, she was excited and confident to move forward into the digital banking era.

Today, most people (and especially Millennials) won't wait for the inefficiency of prior commons practices. In an era when everyone always has a mobile device in their possession, there's no reason that payments to each other can't be immediate, precise, safe and transparent.

PayPal started operating as a preferred source for online money transfers at the end of the last century, but it was their purchase of Venmo in 2014 that truly brought peer-to-peer digital payments into the transparency era. *Forbes* referred to this entrant into one of the most crowded spaces in tech as "**the crown jewel of all finance apps**"[1] because not only does it reflect changing technology, but also changing social and privacy expectations.

Simply put, it's not just a payment tool, it's also a transparent social hub.

When you make a payment with Venmo, your "news feed" reflects what you spent it on and to whom you sent the money. While it's possible to add greater levels of privacy, the default setting is one of openness and transparency. Of course, there are some limitations—users posting transactions for illicit activities may get flagged as inappropriate—but the nearly wholesale embrace of publicizing one's transactions reflects a "new normal."

In other words, despite risking that this level of openness might create a track record and lead to more questions, those embracing the notion that transparency translates to knowledge, growth, and power embrace what may seem to some people as "radical."

The proof is in Venmo's exponential results. The company was acquired for $26.2 million in 2012, then flipped for $800 million in 2013. That seems to have been a prescient investment, as the company's value and usage has continued to surge. In the third quarter of 2018, the volume of payments handled by Venmo surged 78%, to $17 billion.

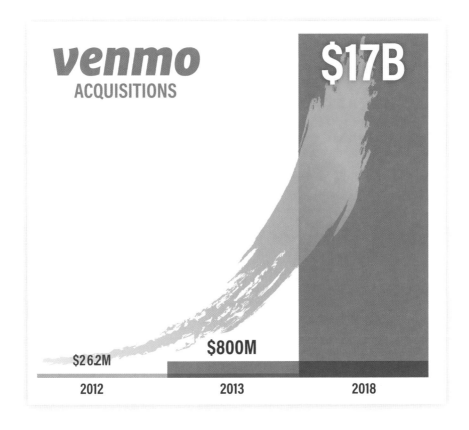

The clumsiness of your friend's cash IOU is over. Now "Venmo it" is a verb in the same way that "Google it" or "take an Uber" have entered the common vernacular—and transparency is a big part of what is driving the new normal.

Once I saw this combination of transparency and technology in action, a light bulb went on in my head. While my generation has much of the political capital and monetary heft within the world, that doesn't mean that we know all the answers. Indeed, one of the hallmarks of many of the technological revolutions during my lifetime has been that it is youth-driven. A good friend of mine, David Roberts, eloquently said, "**If you want to know the future, simply ask it.**" Talking with Millennials is speaking with the future.

We may not always accept that change can come "from the mouths of babes," but there's something about a youthful open mind that (when combined with some of the experience obtained by aging) can provide a clearer lens on the future. With that in mind, I put two and two together and realized that many of the thought leaders whose insights and observations have influenced me the most are not necessarily Millennials themselves but have consistent interaction with younger generations.

Remembering Ric Edelman's anecdote (as described in Chapter 4) about how his 90-year-old mother would never think of questioning a medical doctor's authority—but how current 20- and 30-somethings would do it as a matter of course—I sought out others who might be able to see the evolutionary thought trends that are taking shape.

Specifically, I contacted the following experts:

- Wyatt Andrews, formerly a National Correspondent for CBS News and since 2016 a professor in the Department of Media Studies at the University of Virginia.

- Dr. Rainford Knight, professor of finance at Florida Atlantic University, cofounder of Florida Institute of Finance, and a recognized authority on mergers and acquisitions in a wide range of industries.

- Dr. Laura Carstensen, the founding director of the Stanford Center on Longevity and the principal investigator for the Stanford Life-Span Development Laboratory.

All of them have substantial real-world experience in their fields, enough that their opinions have solidified (but hopefully not calcified), based on empirical and observable evidence. At the same time, they all work at top universities, interacting daily with the best and the brightest of the next generations. From their positions, they are perfectly situated to assess the situation without the typical blinders that most of us wear.

In his classes at UVA, Wyatt Andrews has realized that technology is a major driver in how we receive and digest our news, but only part of the way that we can promote and enhance transparency going forward. We also need to understand those truths. This absolutely shocked him to first take a step back and assess the current landscape.

"Two years ago, when I first started teaching the class—it's literally called 'The News Media', and it's my attempt to coach up their news literacy—I said, 'Watch a TV newscast story. One that's actually on TV. Not something that you get purely off the web. Watch a TV news story from one of the TV broadcasters. Local or national or cable. Don't care.' And two years ago, those students nodded their heads and wrote down the assignment.

"Last spring, I said the same thing," he continued. "'Your assignment for Friday is to watch a television newscast, at least one story over a television newscast. It could be local, national, or cable TV,' which is how my curriculum lays out. I saw dead eyes. **I saw across the spectrum of one-hundred students that they had no idea what I meant by a TV newscast** that you didn't get online.

"I SAW ACROSS THE SPECTRUM OF 100 STUDENTS THAT

THEY HAD NO IDEA WHAT I MEANT BY A TV NEWSCAST."

WYATT ANDREWS, PROFESSOR OF MEDIA STUDIES, UNIVERSITY OF VIRGINIA

"Almost none of them had a subscription to any kind of newspaper. Almost none of them had cable subscriptions because it didn't have anything that they were interested in. Some of them had HBO, but they're watching it off an app, not through a traditional cable subscription. I had to explain to them what television news was as distinct from TV that you watch on your phone. I had to explain to them what a cable subscription was.

"Just think about that. That's the level of how much news literacy we have lost in this country. And they literally do not know the difference between Lester Holt at NBC and Sean Hannity on Fox News. One is a reporter trying to do his job and draw a mass audience. The other is a right-wing commentator who sometimes has a very loose association with facts. And that's an example of the threat that we face as millions of very smart young Americans have no concept of news transparency and what they should trust. They see it all in terms of a box on their phone. And boy, if you don't know that difference organically just from being news consumers, we have a lot of people to educate on this."

> "MILLENNIALS ARE USING THE TECHNOLOGY WITHOUT FULLY UNDERSTANDING **HOW EMPOWERED THEY ARE.**"
>
> DR. RAINFORD KNIGHT
> PROFESSOR OF FINANCE,
> FLORIDA ATLANTIC UNIVERSITY

In the classes he teaches at Florida Atlantic University and around the world, Dr. Knight deals with both executives and Millennials. While both groups may value transparency, their recognition of the issues and the way that they address them is often dissimilar.

"I don't think Millennials are as concerned at this point because they're perhaps distracted by other things," Dr. Knight said. "I think they use technology without being aware of the benefit of transparency. But for older mid-level managers, the executive types, I think this is definitely a concern because in their respective firms, **they're also seeing this adaptation of technology and the move toward being more transparent**. Millennials are using the technology without fully understanding how empowered they are. And they don't fully understand what the pre-app world was like. Now we're in the application world where everything is an app, so you're used to having all this information around. I think that's interesting because they really don't get it— They don't really understand the value of transparency since their phone now allows them to do a lot of things that before people were not able to do."

What does Dr. Laura Carstensen, an expert on longevity and finding ways to increase not only the span of our lives but the quality of them, have to offer younger generations?

She too understands that transparency of information is the key to achieving goals that individuals might not realize for an additional 50, 60, or 70 years. After all, while many Millennials are concerned with their health outcomes, most young people, at least subconsciously, consider themselves invincible. They think that aging and the diseases that accompany it happen to "other people." They assume that there will always be a chance to rectify today's bad health decisions with a pill, a surgery, or another technological advance at some point down the road. To some extent, they're right. On the other hand, we don't know what the world will look like in 50 years, and we don't know all the likely outcomes related to decisions made today. Thus, it's critical that we get the message across to these young people as soon as possible.

In many respects, the need to get this younger generation (and everyone, really) to understand the long-term consequences of early action mirrors the lessons of compound interest that we try to impress on young professionals—saving even modest amounts every year in your 20's will allow you to get far ahead of someone who doesn't start saving until their 30's, even if they put in much greater amounts annually.

It's the beauty of **compound interest** all over again! Whether Albert Einstein said it, or it was merely attributed to him because of his exceptional genius, it's a **concept that impacts everything** we do. Start planning early, make educated decisions from the get-go, and the beneficial results will stream forth exponentially.

Since the age of five, my son's passion in life has always been baseball. Don't remember a time when he didn't have a baseball in his hand every day. As a result of his passion and persistence, he played at Paul VI in Virginia, one of the top high school baseball programs in the country. Then he went on the be part of East Carolina's baseball program. Upon graduating, he joined the New York Yankees to pursue a career in player development. He'd been receptive to good coaching all his life, and while his baseball acumen eventually surpassed mine, as his dad, I felt a responsibility to coach him on the importance of starting to save early.

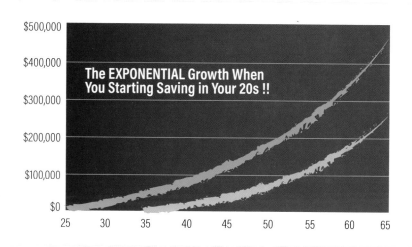

Here's what I said to him: "Guess who has more money at retirement, someone who starts saving at age 20 and saves $200 a month for ten years or someone who starts saving at age 30 and puts away $200 month, but for 30 years?"

Of course, he replied that the person who saved for 30 years would accumulate far more than the one who saved for ten years. He was beyond shocked when I explained that the person who started at age 20 would have twice the amount saved by the age of 60 as the person who started at age 30 and contributed for three times as many years. That simple explanation motivated him to start saving immediately with his first paycheck. This is a beautiful example of how compound interest works for you over the long haul.

THE RULE OF 72

Annual Interest Rate	Rule of 72	Years to Double
4%	72 ÷ 4 =	18.0
5%	72 ÷ 5 =	14.4
6%	72 ÷ 6 =	12.0
7%	72 ÷ 7 =	10.3
8%	72 ÷ 8 =	9.0

Many acquaintances ask me how to double their money. My response is always the same, and it's a question back at them: "Have you ever heard of the 'Rule of 72'?"

The Rule of 72 is a simple way to determine how long it will take your money to double. It doesn't require a high-powered computer or even a calculator. It's an easy mathematical equation. Simply divide 72 into the annual interest rate you expect to earn. This will let you know how long it will take. For example, if you expect to earn 8% annually, divide 72 by eight; the answer is nine. Earning 8% annually on your investment means that it will take nine years to double.

The exciting part of this is we're increasingly able to see which results are wise and which will have long-term beneficial impacts. As Dr. Carstensen said, "Technologies are being developed that will allow us to see relationships between our behavior and our health on a time scale never before possible. Computer scientists are making sensors so tiny they can be **'tattooed' on the skin**. These sensors will monitor respiration, heart rate, blood pressure, glucose, and a range of other functions on a near-continuous basis and communicate that information wirelessly to devices that will integrate and communicate immediate feedback."

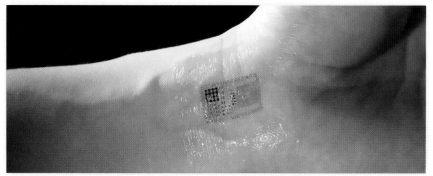

PHOTO SOURCE: https://theconversation.com, John A. Rogers

My kids have been asking me for years if I'd get a tattoo, and I've always answered with a definite "No," but if that prophecy comes to life, I may have to change my answer! See, Millennials know more than we sometimes give them credit for!

But again, this is all about information—how we receive it, who provides it, and how we digest and implement it. That's why I'm so optimistic. So is Dr. Carstensen.

"As a behavioral scientist, I believe that these types of data will instigate behavioral changes in powerful ways," she said. "Today, we tell people to watch their diets, drink moderately, don't smoke, and exercise, but there is considerable distance between the risky behaviors themselves and health outcomes, not to mention a myriad of other potential explanations. Moreover, the outcomes that we communicate are based on averages for the general population. Bottom line: people don't see what smoking a cigarette or eating a burger is doing to their health." In the future, these technologies will allow us to see how healthy and not-so-healthy practices are affecting our bodies.

"In some cases, we'll hear good news because we may not have a typical response. We might be someone who responds well to red meat," Dr. Carstensen continued. "Today's information is telling us almost nothing about ourselves as individuals. Rather, it tells us about large groups of people. New technologies will provide tailored feedback. I have great hope that when we can get that kind of feedback immediately, it will have powerful effects on behavior. I also believe that these advances will allow us to intervene when we're healthy as opposed to waiting until we have developed a disease." Imagine learning that you are near diabetic but not diabetic and that certain foods and not others elevate your glucose. Do you think this would shape your behavior?

All three of these experts will address these issues in greater detail in subsequent chapters, but the bottom line is what they've stressed for all of us: that even if we're dealing with longer horizons for personal growth than ever before, the timeline for addressing some of the issues that confront all of us today may be shrinking.

IT IS **IMPERATIVE** THAT WE SOLVE OUR MOST PRESSING ISSUES SOONER RATHER THAN LATER.

To this end, Wyatt Andrews mentioned a book by Siva Vaidhyanathan, called *Antisocial Media,* and one section in particular. "One of his killer lines is that the problem with Facebook is Facebook. Facebook makes too much money and operates in too many countries and in too many languages to be able to solve this overnight."

In other words, if we are going to tackle these potential impediments and build upon the underlying benefits, then we need to start now, and we need to bring a concerted effort. If we take the wrong path, then the deleterious effects may grow exponentially, but we clearly can head in a much more positive direction.

Despite what he sees as an unnecessarily widespread loss of news literacy, Wyatt remains optimistic. "I think we will figure this out," he said. "I think whether it's online, streaming, broadcast, PBS, wherever, nothing in our character is changing. **There's always going to be a market for really smart news."**

"I don't have any doubt at all about the long term," he concluded. "Somebody smart enough is going to figure out a way to monetize accurate reporting."

By harnessing market-based, regulatory and behavioral incentives, that sort of thinking should guide our path forward in many other disciplines too.

TRANSPARENCY CHANGES EVERYTHING !!

CHAPTER 8 I GENERATIONAL SHIFT

wis·dom

/'wizdəm/

the quality of having
experience, knowledge,
and good judgment; the
quality of being wise.

WHY **IT MATTERS:**

- Our life expectancy will be longer than we think. Insight into the keys to longevity will enable you to unlock a long, high-quality life.
- Consumers and workplaces will increasingly demand transparency.

ADVICE:

- Improve your information intake by learning how to intuit accurate news and discard "fake news."
- Always have an open mind—turning a negative into a positive is a learned habit.
- "When" we start saving can be more important than "how much" we save.

TAKE**AWAYS:**

- We have entered the longevity era—humans are now living exponentially longer than our ancestors.
- The generation before us provides great insights into our future—always be learning.
- Technology is reshaping the medical and health-care industries.

ACTION STEPS**:**

- Create one new longevity habit.
- Consider paying for your news source.
- Save a percentage of every paycheck.
- Save early in life and stick with the plan.

PART TWO
AN EXPONENTIAL WORLD

"The best is
yet to come."

PAUL PAGNATO

TRANSPARENCY WAVE

CHAPTER 9

Get Ready for the Ride of Your Life

With all the confusion over transparency's optimum utilization—or even its objective meaning—it's easy to be baffled by how we should think, implement, and embrace transparency.

Consider again the 6Ts of Exponential Transparency:

1	**TRANSPARENCY STANDARDS**	**4**	TRANSPARENT COST
2	**TERMS**	**5**	TRUTH
3	TOTAL ACCOUNTABILITY	**6**	TRUST

If, at a time when technology is moving at an exponential pace, we can't even settle on **who** or **what** is transparent, or **how much** transparency provides the greatest good for the greatest number of people, it's easy to throw up your hands, bury your head in the sand (choose your own metaphor for willful blindness!), and just "go with the flow."

The reality is that the natural inclination for most people is to go with the flow. My life experiences, observations, and mentors have taught me to reject that inherent tendency and be continuously positive. As discussed earlier, I call this **"PMA," which stands for Positive Mental Attitude**.

There is only one thing we can control every day—our attitude. As Viktor Frankl wrote in the seminal book *Man's Search for Meaning*, "Everything can be taken from a man but one thing: the last of the human freedoms—to choose one's attitude in any given set of circumstances, to choose one's own way."

Of course, there will always be uncontrollable variables—traffic, the economy, our parents and siblings, the price of gasoline, tax rates, federal and state laws, or if our commercial flight is on time. In the face of those unchangeable factors, though, we can always control our attitude. A dear friend of mine woke up every day with gratitude saying two words: "Thank you." He was one of the happiest and most grateful individuals I ever knew. It didn't matter if he was sick or healthy, in good times and bad, his PMA allowed him to take every situation head-on and emerge smiling.

THERE IS ONLY **ONE THING WE CAN CONTROL** EVERY DAY—
OUR ATTITUDE.

There are things each of us can do to remain on track and have PMA. The first: express gratitude and thank people (strangers, acquaintances, family members) for whatever it is they may have done. It could be a favor, a smile, or something bigger, but when someone adds a point of light to your life, let them know how it made you feel.

Expressing gratitude gives you a positive mental outlook and a positive attitude makes you happy.

And it doesn't cost any money!

Anybody can express gratitude. Anybody.

It could be as simple as opening and holding the door.

It could be as simple as saying "Hi!" to somebody on the street.

Resolve to give more hugs or find another way to put a smile on someone's face. There are so many ways to add value to other peoples' lives. Just having a dialogue or a conversation with someone who might be struggling—a simple three- to five-minute conversation—can change their day and their life, and the resulting ripple effects will come back to you tenfold. See, there's always an exponential effect!

Having PMA is a habit, just as having a negative mental attitude is a habit. Barbara Fredrickson, a professor at the University of North Carolina, is one of the world's leading experts on positivity. Her research indicates that the **prescription for happiness is a ratio of positive to negative emotions of greater than 3:1**. In other words, we need at least three heartfelt positive emotions to overcome each deep negative emotion. That ratio is the tipping point that will determine our odds of flourishing or languishing. Positive emotions trigger upward spirals toward emotional well-being.

Dating back to the Neanderthal period, human beings have used mirroring as a means of learning and adapting. Through biological programming, we are inclined to imitate one another—our body language, facial expressions, voice tone and pace and, perhaps most importantly, our emotions. Through its neurons, our brain processes the actions we observe of others as if we are experiencing them ourselves. The simplest and most common example of this is that when one person yawns, often the people around them yawn as well.

You may not think that yawning in unison is an evolutionary advantage, but we can take this reality and use it to our benefit. Being positive around people affects not only your own well-being, but also that of the people around you. When I'm with someone who is negative, I listen, express empathy, and then share something positive. Success is failure turned inside out. Failing is actually a positive thing, placing you one step closer to success. It's almost always a necessary stepping-stone on the journey to success.

My wife and I regularly visit wounded troops at Walter Reed National Military Medical Center and at the Fisher House. We invite these young men into our home during the holidays and bring them to sporting events. What I'm about to share with you will blow your mind. These young men have seen unspeakable things. They're often missing limbs and go through repeated surgeries. One soldier, who calls my wife "Mom," has had over 80 surgeries. Despite having every reason to be depressed, virtually each time we are in their presence, we revel in their positive mental attitudes. They focus on the future, they focus on the positive, they focus on what they can do versus what they are no longer capable of doing. These soldiers' positive attitudes are contagious and make you feel good every time. If they can have PMA, so can you.

It may run contrary to popular opinion, but I have no doubt that all of us can control our stress. One lesson I learned in business and then applied to my personal relationships is something I call a "non-acceptable." If a family member, peer, or friend is doing something that's stressing me

---

BEING POSITIVE AROUND PEOPLE AFFECTS
NOT ONLY YOUR OWN WELL-BEING, BUT ALSO THAT OF
THE PEOPLE AROUND YOU.

out, eventually I get to a point where I'm not going to tolerate it. At that point, it becomes nonacceptable. I disengage, often removing myself from the situation or the relationship altogether. The best strategy I've found is one of extreme transparency. I'll stop and tell the other person, in polite but clear terms, "This bothers me. I'm not good with this. Please don't do that again!"

The goal is to nip it at the right time. None of us like conflict and confrontation, and it prevents us from being transparent, but the result is often a situation that quietly escalates to a point of no return. With that comes stress.

During these periods of elevated tension verging on stress, I'll try to go to my "happy place." It's a method that I've used extensively in yoga and in situations when hitting a wall with a physical challenge. Pick a location or activity or feeling that makes you happiest and visualize it. It's that simple. For me, my happy place is out on the water, fishing for bass. It's a pastime that is relaxing, engaging, and challenging, and it's the venue in which I feel the greatest level of inner peace. When getting into a stressful or confrontational situation, I'm able to excise myself from it simply by visualizing a perfect day on the lake, out catching a few fish, as far from the conflict as possible. It centers me.

Another happy place for me is Southern Italy, where my family roots lies and where many members of the extended family still live. It is one of the most beautiful places on the planet. In thinking about multiple past

CALABRIA, ITALY

trips there, and the many more to come, it just helps block everything else out.

Meditation is a fantastic tool for filtering out the negative thoughts that all of us experience so eventually it won't just be a "filter," but a garbage disposal getting rid of negativity wholesale.

You don't need to meditate for an hour or even a half hour. We all have "real lives" with obligations and time commitments and things we want to do. But it's also normal to have some sort of semi- constant mental chatter in your head. If a substantial portion of that is negative, don't despair. You're normal. You're human. It's part of having a functioning mind—even when you're in the midst of one dialogue, your brain is constantly analyzing additional thoughts, judgments and data points. Some of them may be positive and some may be negative, but meditation is a beautiful mechanism for filtering out the noise and maintaining the signal. It teaches you that when a negative thought enters your brain, you can acknowledge it, accept it, and then let it go.

Ten minutes of meditation provides a good "flush." That little bit of effort will let the pressure, stress, and black clouds fly away.

You can have ominous clouds cluttering your brain, or you can have white fluffy clouds lifting it up. That's a choice. It really is.

What else?

How about taking a simple walk?

No one will deny that exercise is beneficial for keeping the physical body in shape and the mental processes sharp, but too many people assume that the stimulation is only beneficial if you run a marathon, pump heavy iron for hours, or swim dozens of laps. Properly supervised and with appropriate training, those methods can be beneficial, but it's not an "all or nothing" endeavor. Too many people say, "I don't have time to run ten miles, so I'll just stay at home and watch TV." That's a recipe for disaster, and you're only fooling yourself if you try to convince yourself otherwise.

It's undisputed that all of us have hormones that get stimulated when we exercise, but we're not willing to undertake the many steps necessary to get to the point of physical perfection. We see an ideal, and we see reality, and any difference between the two leads us to inaction or negativity.

MEDITATION TEACHES YOU THAT WHEN A NEGATIVE THOUGHT ENTERS YOUR BRAIN, YOU CAN **ACKNOWLEDGE IT, ACCEPT IT, AND THEN LET IT GO**.

The better strategy is to make the most of the time you do have. Work in a suit, no gym nearby? When you feel that stress coming on, head outside and take a five-to-ten-minute walk. It might not solve your problem directly, but you'll feel better and it'll put you in a better position to solve the problem using your mental toolbox. The black storm clouds will dissipate, and they'll be replaced by the white fluffy ones—or maybe by pure sunshine!

Another way to enhance mental clarity is through your diet. Nutritionists and doctors could write chapters on this, so I'll keep it brief and limit it to the dietary factor that has affected me the most. Literally, you are what you eat, and the biggest gremlin I've found is sugar. There's consensus that it's a mind-killer in addition to bloating your belly and messing up your metabolism.

What happens is that when you ingest a lot of sugar, you get stimulated. That's good. It often leads to positive thought and positive energy.

But it's a false positive—thus the term "sugar high."

When that buzz goes away—and it always goes away unless you continue to feed the beast, which creates problems of its own—your blood sugar drops. At that point, you kind of hit a wall and all that positive energy is transformed into something quite harmful. The fall is worse than if you'd never had the sugar in the first place.

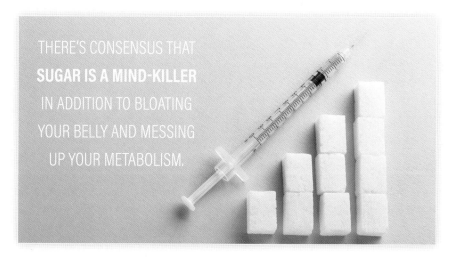

THERE'S CONSENSUS THAT **SUGAR IS A MIND-KILLER** IN ADDITION TO BLOATING YOUR BELLY AND MESSING UP YOUR METABOLISM.

Making this even worse is that sugar is one of the most addictive substances on the planet. Some say it's harder to kick than cocaine, and I'm sure a part of that is psychological. When you were a child, good behavior was rewarded with a cookie or by going out for ice cream. It's in your brain that there is a "sweet reward" for achievement. The quicker you can dull that connection, the better it will be for your positive outlook.

The final manageable tool that's available to all of us is our sleep clock. Many of us require a full eight hours of restful sleep to operate at maximum efficiency. Albert Einstein reportedly slept eight to nine hours a day. Block out the time to sleep or take a power nap but be sure to take care of your rhythms before your brain gets worn down. If you don't, the black clouds will infiltrate. A little bit of solid, dedicated pillow time can prevent that.

All these steps involve keeping your brain clear and removing negativity. Many people assume we're hard-wired the way we are and that anything short of perfection is failure. This gives them license to disclaim control.

Don't fall victim to that sort of thinking!

It doesn't mean you won't get caught in ruts along the journey. That's going to happen to everybody, but by maintaining a toolbox that allows you to escape or overcome those ruts, you'll flatten out the lows and heighten the highs.

That's why I end emails with PMA. I'm trying to share the love, and it makes me feel good. It puts me in a good mindset and I'm hoping others see that, and it puts a smile on their face, and they pay it forward. It's contagious—positivity feeds on positivity and negativity feeds on negativity, so at any given time if more people are enticed to be in that positive frame of mind, we can't help but be living in a better place.

There's a direct connection between PMA and exponentiality. There will always be "glass half full" and "glass half empty" people. While there are exceptions to the rules, for the most part, the brains processing things as "half empty" have a harder time wrapping themselves around exponential concepts. It's much harder for them. Thinking positively is akin to leaning forward, while thinking negatively has you back on your heels in a defensive mode.

The more you lean forward, the more you tilt yourself toward understanding and valuing the positive power of exponential thinking and advances. It enables you to let go of the negativity more easily. There's still a seat at the table for the skeptics—in fact, on every board I've ever sat on, I have valued having at least one "glass half empty" member because they balance me out. They keep me honest. They keep my exuberance in check when it needs to be checked. But the valuable ones are willing to let go of their skepticism when it is proved to be unwarranted.

PMA is a choice.

Transparency is a choice.

In my experience, exponential growth is the result of those two choices.

How does PMA tie into transparency and the exponential pace of change we are experiencing?

For every negative thought a human has about transparency, there are at least three positives occurring, creating that necessary tipping point. Transparency is saving peoples' lives on a daily basis. Let's look at three examples:

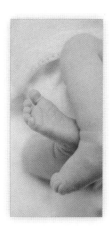

1. DNA TESTING OF NEWBORNS

People have long been concerned about the ancillary effects of testing newborns for genetic disorders. They feared that a newborn's DNA could be used against them one day; for example, say the newborn commits a crime later in life and their DNA is used as proof for conviction. Or perhaps they would be discriminated against in the workplace for some immutable characteristic. We've reached a point where the vast array of positives is outweighing those concerns. Every day newborn babies are cured of life-threatening genetic disorders as a direct result of testing, saving their lives and making them more comfortable. In the state of California alone, over 2,500 newborns have been treated for genetic disorders in the past two years. In the past, that would not have occurred.

2. GOVERNMENT TRANSPARENCY

People have long struggled over the extent to which governments should be transparent. We want to avoid conflicts of interests or inappropriate behavior as, for example, complete transparency to the media might threaten the security of the country. On balance, though, the most transparent countries in the world have the least amount of corruption. Over the last five years, 368 journalists have been killed; 96% of those deaths occurred in countries below the corruption policy index average.[1]

3. AUTONOMOUS VEHICLES

People are concerned that autonomous vehicles are not safe. Over the last two years, more than 37,000 people died from automobile accidents in the United States, an average of one-hundred deaths a day. Globally, 1.2 million deaths occur from automobile accidents; 94% of those accidents result from human error. Those deaths translate to a rate of one death per 80 million miles driven, while Tesla cars equipped with autopilot experience one death per 320 million miles. That makes them four times safer on average. It's no wonder Teslas are considered the safest cars in the world.

Even the most positive human beings experience ups and downs due to life's challenges, and it's not atypical for anyone to get into an occasional funk. I call this "getting into the gap."

Let me share a process my coach **Dan Sullivan** taught me 20 years ago to minimize and overcome these down periods. It's called the **"21 Day Positive Focus."** The basic premise is that it takes a human being 21 days to create a new habit. My first experience with this occurred when my son was in third grade. Every Friday the class would take a 20-question spelling test, and my child would perform exceptionally, never missing more than one or two out of 20. Afterward, though, he would focus on the one or two missed as opposed to celebrating the 18 or 19 correct answers. My child would come home in the "gap"—in a funk and not happy—so we started working with the tools of the 21 Day Positive Focus.

Each night before going to bed, we would write down five positive things that happened during the day. When we first started, my son was unable to come up with anything positive. I would ask: "Do you love your mother? Did you go to school? Did you do your homework? Did you help anyone today? Do you love your sister? Did you do any exercise today? Did you eat heathy today?" Starting the second week, he would quickly have his five positive focus items. After that tipping point, he'd be out of the gap and would enjoy a positive mental attitude. Today, I refuse to go to bed with any negative thoughts rattling around in my head. If I've had a tough day, my wife and I will do a positive focus together.

While working diligently every day to view people, events, and issues through the PMA lens, proper utilization requires work:

- Understand the issues.
- Ferret out the realistic fact patterns.
- Understand others' motivations.
- Understand my own motivations.

Most critically, meld all of that into a comprehensive world view that allows you to be simultaneously objective and proactive. That can be scary. It can be uncertain. If you choose to follow this path—and I hope you will—you'll need to protect yourself and others against improper assumptions. That's realistic, but if you allow yourself to veer too far in the direction of caution or fear, it may also hamper your ability to make the most of the opportunities that are stretching out before you.

Remember, transparency is the filter through which the path forward will shoot, but exponentiality is the product—or suite of products—that will be pushed through that filter.

My goal is to help you ride that wave of transparency, taking it to places that as recently as a few years ago would not have seemed possible. In fact, some of the things you will experience sooner than later may still seem unlikely or unthinkable as you read this. Open your mind and get ready to discard fear and uncertainty and to embrace the possibilities that are about to become open to not just a select few lucky people, but to the world at large.

Let's look back at the last 100 years and then forward the next ten years. One hundred years ago, in 1909, the world produced one major invention: the toaster. That's it. You could take your bread and toast it.

Now we have one new invention every hour, and almost all of them do a lot more than toast your bread. One hundred years ago, the first automobiles were rolled out and the first telegraphs were on route. Most of the population worked on farms. The world did not have—in fact, could likely not even conceive of—cell phones, airlines, computers, and the Internet, among many other things. The current period of exponential rate of change is placing everything into overdrive and the pace of change over the next ten years will be far greater than those we experienced over the last hundred years.

TODAY:
1 NEW INVENTION
EVERY HOUR

1909 - The Toaster

HERE'S A GLIMPSE OF WHAT THINGS MAY LOOK LIKE
TEN YEARS FROM NOW:

- 3D printing will revolutionize traditional manufacturing and the corresponding market will go from $7 billion to $94 billion.

- Genome sequencing could become a clinical standard of care. CRISPR is a powerful DNA editing tool capable of addressing all monogenic diseases, and that market alone could generate $75 billion in annual revenues.

- Travel could go autonomous sooner than most think. The market for autonomous taxi networks could reach $7 trillion. Electric vehicles should be cheaper than gas-powered cars due to declining battery costs. Digital wallet providers could surpass the largest financial institutions. Venmo, a remarkably recent entrant, is already the 4th largest, just behind Wells Fargo, Bank of America, and JP Morgan.

- The Internet added $10 trillion in equity capitalization over the last 20 years. Deep learning could add another $20 trillion over the next 20 years. Collaborative robots working alongside humans could become the standard.[2]

Get ready for the ride of your life!!

TRANSPARENCY CHANGES EVERYTHING !!

Get ready for the ride of your life!!

PERSPECTIVES

CHAPTER 9 | GET READY FOR THE RIDE OF YOUR LIFE

change

/CHānj/

make or become different.

IT TAKES A HUMAN BEING **21 DAYS TO CREATE A NEW HABIT.**

WHY **IT MATTERS:**

- In the next ten years, humans will experience more change than in the last 100 years. The impact to human beings, society, and our personal lives will be something never experienced before. The level of transparency will be exponential in all aspects of our lives.

ADVICE:

- Attitude is the one thing we can control every day, so choose positivity.
- Your attitude impacts everyone around you.
- The first negative thought is a thought to failure.

TAKE**AWAYS:**

- You can make a difference—every day. Expressing gratitude creates happiness.
- You need three positive emotions to override the influence of every negative emotion.
- Sugar is the most addictive substance known to mankind.

ACTION STEPS**:**

- Always maintain a Positive Mental Attitude (PMA).
- Perform a 21 Day Positive Focus when you feel like you're in the "gap."
- Create your nonacceptables.
- Go to your happy place mentally, meditate and exercise daily, be mindful of what you eat, and get a good night's sleep.
- Help others be positive and transparent.

"EXPONENTIALITY IS HERE, AND IT'S HERE TO STAY."

PAUL PAGNATO

CHAPTER 10

The Exponential Era

Vint Cerf earned a PhD from UCLA, where the topic of his dissertation was "Multiprocessors, Semaphores, and a Graph Model of Computation," so you probably wouldn't expect a few numbers or charts to faze him.

If those bona fides aren't enough, how about these? Cerf has earned honorary degrees from two dozen or so international universities around the world. In 2005, President George W. Bush awarded him the Presidential Medal of Freedom. He's also a member of the National Inventors Hall of Fame, the Internet Hall of Fame, and has been issued awards by the French Légion d'honneur and the United Kingdom Royal Society.

That's just a small taste of the ways that he has been recognized for his massive contributions to the United States, to technology, and to the world. There are even unsubstantiated rumors that the character of the architect in *The Matrix* series of movies is based upon him.

What did he do to deserve those honors?

Nothing more than invent the Internet.

Yes, Cerf and partner Bob Kahn, "The Fathers of the Internet," were major drivers in the creation of the single most transformative technology of the 20th and 21st centuries, the one that continues to drive innovation at a breakneck pace. Neither one would likely ever be presumptuous enough to say that, but for their involvement, the Internet never would've been invented or discovered. But it's clear that their research conducted with the United States' Defense Advanced Research Projects Agency (DARPA) catalyzed the development of the life-changing tool that we all use constantly in modern life.

Given that resumé, and the brain that made it possible, you'd expect that Cerf would offer up some complex and highfalutin' explanation when asked to explain exponentiality. Instead, Cerf leaned on popular culture, specifically on an episode of the original *Star Trek* first broadcast in 1967 (before the "semi-official" introduction of what would become the Internet) called "The Trouble with Tribbles."

For those of you who aren't sci-fi fanatics and haven't seen the episode, the pertinent part involves Tribbles, little fluffy critters, one of which is given as a gift to a crew member of the USS Enterprise. There's only one problem—that cute little creature has a propensity to reproduce rapidly due to its ability to self-fertilize. 30 years later, to quote a character from that episode: "They do nothing but consume food and breed. If you feed that thing more than the smallest morsel, in a few hours you'll have ten Tribbles, then a hundred—then a thousand."

Pretty soon, the Enterprise was threatened to be overrun by what at first seemed to be a harmless gift. The Tribbles worked their way into duct systems, seemed likely to eat up all the grain being transported, and occupied every available area of the spaceship.

Cerf is a major Trekkie, so years ago, his colleagues decided to play a trick on him.

One day, they placed a stuffed (allegedly non-reproducing) Tribble in his office before he arrived at work.

The next day there were two.

Then four.

And so on until they threatened to take over the whole space.

With daily doubling, that takes a surprisingly short amount of time. It's the same as the "doubling of a penny" example given earlier. Our brain's intuition is that it doesn't seem like it should add up to much in any reasonable period, but it quickly grows into millions of dollars. Another example that I've commonly seen is that if you take 30 steps of a meter apiece, you'll travel a total of 30 meters (even those of us who didn't invent the Internet can figure that one out). If you could figure out a way to double that stride with each step, after 30 steps you'd have gone around the **earth 26 times**. That's a remarkable difference. The bottom line: always take the exponential option.

There's nothing wrong with linear growth, but it's far slower, and a greater slog to the finish line. If you can find a way to jumpstart things in any field exponentially, your progress will literally keep itself moving forward.

That doesn't mean that exponentiality is good in and of itself. The concept itself is qualitatively agnostic—and there are plenty of examples of exponentiality in action where the result is a net negative. Take, for instance, a Ponzi scheme (aka, "pyramid scheme"), where someone defrauds investors and to keep the scam going pays back early investors with money from later dupes while growing the base dramatically. The "pyramid" grows exponentially, with more and more people occupying the bottom levels, until the bottom literally falls out. Its growth is unsustainable. Others would say the same thing about multi-level marketing efforts, many of which remain popular today, in which the goal is not necessarily to sell the product yourself, but rather to develop "downstream" sources of revenue. They can only truly do well when they develop their own downstream underlings, and before you know it, the pool of available recruits is tapped out.

There are examples of exponentiality that might give the word a bad connotation, but given my PMA mantra, I'm of the opinion that **right now we are in the greatest period of positive exponential growth that the world has ever seen.**

WE ARE IN THE **GREATEST PERIOD OF POSITIVE EXPONENTIAL GROWTH** THAT THE WORLD HAS EVER SEEN.

There are so many great developments—many of them stemming from technological advances—that make this the case. Whether it's artificial intelligence, the study of longevity, or the cars we drive, the exponential era that we are living in is cooking much faster than people appreciate or understand.

That doesn't mean it's all blowing up at once. After talking to experts from all those fields, I'm starting to think that the collective upward curve really started in the 1980's. The groundwork for each of these advances was laid much earlier than when we started truly recognizing their fruits. Machine learning goes all the way back to 1956, but we really started applying it 30 or so years later.

Believe it or not, the first autonomous vehicle applications went online in the 1980's. Most Americans never heard of blockchain until certain cryptocurrencies started to dominate the news late in 2017, but its history can be traced back to 1991. It's the same with the Internet—when Cerf and Kahn were working on it in the late 1960s, the tools we have today were just a dream, but even technologically savvy citizens were not really aware of what the Internet might offer until sometime in the 1990's. There were certainly a few early adopters, but they were probably outnumbered by people who thought it was a passing fad or could not be integrated into their daily lives.

Only now are we really seeing the transformative abilities of these advances. We are entering an exponential era. While in the past we've certainly had exponential developments, never have we had so many disparate industries and fields reaching peak exponentiality at the same time.

WE ARE ENTERING AN **EXPONENTIAL** ERA.

In a linear increase, the amount goes up at a predictable uniform pace during a given time period. One year you have two units of computing power. The next year you have four. The following year you have six and so on. The pace of the increase never accelerates. Viewed on X and Y axes, it's a straight line. Exponential growth might look the same way—at first. You go from two to four to eight to 16. It's just deceptive enough to appear linear. Then the afterburners kick in. You go to 32 then 64, then 128 then 256 and so on. The angle of the line you're plotting starts to skyrocket. The change can be so rapid that it appears deceptively misleading.

I've often thought of **exponentiality being tied to a 10x increase**. That rule might not hold for each of the fields we examine in this book during a given time period. They might increase by 4x, 5x, or 20x, but the point is that they are moving off the charts and it is becoming increasingly common to need to rescale a given chart to fit the data.

Of course, not all these fields are accelerating at the same pace, nor can acceleration continue indefinitely. Rather than looking like a "hockey stick," some advances will eventually come to resemble more of an "S" shape. However, as a technologist, a futurist, a historian, and someone who wants to eke every bit of enjoyment and education out of life possible, I'm convinced that we are at "the curve in the hockey stick" (sometimes referred to as "the bend in the knee") in more of these fields at once than at any other time in modern history—or possibly in human history.

Exponential growth in areas that are going to affect your life will be explained in the coming chapters. We will delve into longevity and artificial intelligence and blockchain, among others. Before moving on to those exciting-but-weighty topics, however, I'll help you understand the importance of exponentiality in your financial planning—my particular area of expertise.

There's a famous quote attributed to Albert Einstein, one of the smartest human beings to ever walk the earth: "Compound interest is the eighth wonder of the world. Compound interest is the most powerful force in the universe. He who understands it, earns it; he who doesn't, pays it."

There's some debate about whether old Albert said that, but the fact that it's ascribed to him reflects the fact that many educated and wise people believe that one statement to carry lots of meaning. In the financial industry, it's as if the concept came down on a set of stone tablets. In short, if you put away a certain amount of money each year and let it grow by the amount you contribute, maybe with a boost from some small amount of interest, you might build a meager nest egg. Then again, it might not even keep up with inflation.

On the other hand, if you put away that same amount each year (starting as early as possible, I hope), and get your money to work for you, building wealth through proper investments, you'll be surprised at how quickly it can grow. Earlier I introduced you to the "Rule of 72," a simplified manner of figuring out how long it will take for an investment to double—by dividing 72 by the annual rate of return. If you're getting 2%, it'll take 36 years to double, while at 10% it will take just over seven years.

If you think that a slight difference in the return that you earn doesn't matter, divide 72 by 8% and 9% rates of return. How would you like your money to double a whole year earlier? That could mean retiring earlier, or paying off your kids' college, or it could just give your money a head start on the next round of doubling.

Exponentiality is not going to wait for us. The technological advances on the cusp will benefit all of us in many ways, but there's also a chance that you'll be left behind. You need to change your way of thinking, your habits, and your behaviors—you need to adopt transparency as a way of life. You don't want to be left behind. Exponentiality is here and it's here to stay.

TRANSPARENCY CHANGES EVERYTHING !!

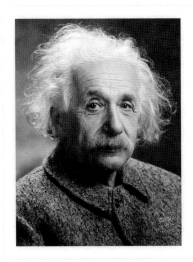

"COMPOUND INTEREST IS THE EIGHTH WONDER OF THE WORLD. COMPOUND INTEREST IS THE MOST POWERFUL FORCE IN THE UNIVERSE. HE WHO UNDERSTANDS IT, EARNS IT; HE WHO DOESN'T, PAYS IT."

ALBERT EINSTEIN

CHAPTER 10 | THE EXPONENTIAL ERA

trans·for·ma·tion

/tran(t)sfər'māSH(ə)n/

a thorough or dramatic change in form or appearance.

PHYSICS

the induced or spontaneous change of one
element into another by a nuclear process.

TRANSPARENCY WAVE

WHY **IT MATTERS:**

- We are in the midst of the largest transformation in human history, transitioning from linear growth to exponential growth.

ADVICE:

- We are what we think—begin thinking exponentially.

- We are what we say—begin speaking exponentially.

TAKE**AWAYS:**

- Anything the human mind can conceive the human being can achieve.

- Compound interest is the eighth wonder of the world and the most powerful force in the universe. If you understand it, you can earn it.

ACTION STEPS:

- Open your mind to big thoughts.

- Start thinking exponentially rather than linearly in all aspects of your life.

- Think exponentially about your personal relationships, health, longevity, career, education, financial well-being, and your impact on other human beings.

"THE IMPACT OF SINGULARITY
WILL SPUR THE GREATEST CHANGES
TO HUMAN CIVILIZATION IN HISTORY."

RAY KURZWEIL

TRANSPARENCY WAVE

CHAPTER 11

Singularity and Exponentiality

Now that you've grasped the concepts of transparency and exponentiality, let's consider some examples and fields that will have the opportunity to make the greatest impact. If you embrace and attack them head-on, they will change the way you process forever.

Much of this thinking has been influenced by my participation in Singularity University's Executive Program, their Global Summits, and the amazing faculty. Singularity University (SU) was founded by two brilliant and visionary futurists, Ray Kurzweil and Peter Diamandis. Their **Massive Transformative Purpose (MTP) is to positively impact one billion lives**.

SU serves both to identify the problems and opportunities that will define our future, and to harness them for the good of society. The name "singularity" comes from Kurzweil, who wrote that artificial intelligence—or actually "artificial superintelligence"—will serve as the launching point for major technological growth, which in turn will spur the greatest changes to human civilization in history.

PETER DIAMANDIS & RAY KURZWEIL
COFOUNDERS,
SINGULARITY
UNIVERSITY

While some equally visionary thinkers have expressed concern about the possibility of singularity—arguing that its harm could hamper or even eclipse its benefits—SU has harnessed the brains of many of our generation's greatest thinkers, innovators, and intellectuals to work to avoid that fate. The collective brainpower there is unprecedented and while I've accomplished a great deal in my life, I still find myself in awe every time attending or corresponding with one or more members of the group. The inspiration has led to speaking engagements at their Global Summits and leading the SU chapter for the Metro Washington, DC area.

At times, it's like drinking from a fire hose—the knowledge and information is coming so fast and furiously that you can't help but need to slow things down to fully digest ideas expressed. At the same time, it's good practice for the world we live in, where innovations are developing, arriving, and being displaced so quickly that a big part of life is learning to integrate that rapid fire flow of information. Think of it this way: we went from LP records to cassettes to CDs to MP3s to Alexa in the span of 40 or 50 years. Now, a similar categorical technological evolution might take four or five years, one-tenth of the prior timeline. If you blink, you could miss an entire generation, or more.

I fully expect that those timelines will be condensed even further in the years to come. That's the "knee of the curve" or the "curve of the hockey stick" in a nutshell.

How is this going to affect you?

Well, like Kurzweil and Diamandis believe, artificial intelligence (AI) will be the primary driver of these changes. Are you using Alexa or Siri or voice-to-text these days? If so, you are already riding this wave, along with millions if not billions of other people worldwide. Unlike discrete innovations of the past, this evolution is going to have a multiplier effect.

Think of how fire, the wheel, the airplane, television, and the Internet all made the world smaller, and at the same time gave rise to many more technologies and opportunities. That's AI, except now we're multiplying all the world's past knowledge—so "x" becomes not "x+1" or even "2x," but rather "10x," which in turn becomes "100x" and so on and so on, to heights previously unimaginable.

The result of this growth will not just be for specific changes— a cure for cancer, a way for civilians to travel to Mars, and flying self-driving cars— but rather the multiplied offspring of each of those changes. We can't possibly imagine everything we'll encounter in your or my lifetime, four or five technological iterations down the road, simply because the things that will happen tomorrow are similarly unprecedented.

As Peter Diamandis said, **"Creating abundance is not about creating a life of luxury for everybody on this planet; it's about creating a life of possibility."**

Like SU itself, my goal is to have a Massive Transformative Purpose (MTP), to affect as many lives as possible in the most positive, life-affirming manner possible. That starts here.

By introducing the basics of AI, genomics, longevity developments, and blockchain, I hope to give you the inspiration and tools to investigate next steps and develop your own view of the future.

You can and will live in it, and you can and should look to impact it positively. Consider this book a challenge and an opportunity to do just that.

TRANSPARENCY CHANGES EVERYTHING !!

PERSPECTIVES

CHAPTER 11 | SINGULARITY

sin·gu·lar·i·ty

/siNG'yə'lerədē/

a point at which a function takes an infinite value, especially in space-time when matter is infinitely dense, as at the center of a black hole.

"TRANSPARENCY IS THE FUTURE, AND IT'S **BEAUTIFUL**."

PAUL PAGNATO

WHY **IT MATTERS:**

- We need to identify the problems and opportunities that will define our future and harness them for the good of society.

ADVICE:

- Embrace change and lean into the future. It's beautiful!

- Artificial intelligence will be the primary driver of change.

TAKE**AWAYS:**

- Singularity is coming.

- The new multiplier is 10x.

- Creating abundance is about creating a life of possibilities.

ACTION STEPS**:**

- Consider attending a Singularity University Global Summit.

- Determine your Massive Transformative Purpose (MTP).

- Embrace technology in a new way.

"FEAR IS THE **NUMBER ONE OBSTACLE** PEOPLE FACE IN BEING TRANSPARENT."

PAUL PAGNATO

CHAPTER 12

Facing Fear

With all the opportunities that lie ahead of us, this is an amazing time to be alive. We can fully expect to live longer than prior generations, to enjoy greater prosperity, comfort, and luxury, and to be able to shape our futures in the image that we desire.

Despite that positive lens, when you describe some of the changes, the first responses are negative.

- Tell someone who is used to the idea of a life expectancy of 80 years that they could live to be 150, and they might snap back, "But what would the quality of life be?" or "I don't want to live in a nursing home for 70 years, destitute and wearing a diaper."

- Tell someone that the presence of artificial intelligence in everyday life will greatly expand over the next decade, and they're likely to complain about the "surveillance state" or express fear over the possibility that robots will take over our lives and control our actions.

- Tell someone who relies on fiat currency cash, or someone who has had their credit card information compromised, that blockchain technology is going to revolutionize how we conduct our financial affairs and make transactions comparatively "frictionless," and they're likely to recall past bubbles in which a few people got rich while a substantial contingent of everyday citizens lost their shirts.

I don't mean to make light of the average person's concerns. Indeed, at the front of every technological revolution there have been swindlers, hustlers, and snake oil salesmen who have taken advantage of others' relative lack of sophistication. We all remember times we have been hoodwinked or bested by others who benefitted from an imbalance of information.

Remember **Bernie Madoff**? He took advantage of a group of people who were generally sophisticated investors, selling them a Ponzi scheme (an example of the bad kind of exponentiality) and got away with it for a long time. Yes, he ended up in prison, but his victims lost billions of dollars.

SOURCE: *New York Times*

With examples like that etched in our minds, it's natural to be cautious. We remember the failures and the hardships—like the recession that started in 2007—rather than the years of prosperity that followed on its heels.

TRANSPARENCY WAVE

If fear is natural, how do we use it to protect ourselves while also preventing it from limiting our opportunities?

In real-life terms, how can we harness it to avoid falling prey to someone like Bernie Madoff, but not end up with our money under the mattress, unprotected, and unable to benefit from compound interest?

Where is that middle ground?

Well, it varies for all of us. Some of us have high levels of risk tolerance, while others are more risk-averse. Some of that is born into you while another portion is likely the result of personal life experiences. And, of course, some of it is situational—if you have $10 million in the bank, you might be willing to give up $100,000 for the chance at another million, whereas if you're dirt-poor without a clear path to getting out of debt, the guarantee of one-hundred grand will far outweigh that outside chance at a much larger pot of money.

No matter your situation, fear can be used as a valuable motivating tool and a protective shield if you don't let it get out of hand. That dates back to our caveman days.

At each watershed moment in human history, **the people who have emerged on top have been those who were most adaptable in the face of "extinction."** A blacksmith 100 years ago had a leg up on others in terms of the ability to repair motorcars. If he hesitated, he got left behind, but if he harnessed his fear of the new, he could come out ahead. Same with the typewriter repairman or the TV antenna installer of recent decades who were made obsolete—they had a *choice* between obsolescence and embracing opportunity.

Take a careful accounting of your skills and vulnerabilities so when change comes, you're ready to conquer fear by utilizing the former and minimizing the negative impact of the latter.

As I pondered the role of fear in my life, I was reminded of a fishing trip from a few years ago. We were cruising the inside passage of Alaska in style on a boat with multiple cabins, catered gourmet meals, fine wines from around the world, and an onboard naturalist to educate us at every turn. It was a safe and curated view of the environment around us. We were stretching our boundaries—but carefully.

> WHEN CHANGE COMES YOU MUST BE READY TO **CONQUER FEAR** BY UTILIZING YOUR SKILLS AND MINIMIZING THE NEGATIVE IMPACT OF YOUR VULNERABILITIES.

The larger boat had staterooms and all the comforts of home, and we could have been quite happy without ever leaving the safety of that cocoon. We were still immersed in the natural world, closer to all sorts of amazing, photogenic creatures and scenery than most people will ever be. It was a bucket list trip for the ages.

Still, we wanted more. The boat towed a dinghy, which allowed for access to smaller streams and bays where larger boats could not travel. As an avid fisherman I was excited to learn that some of the waters we were traversing contained **Dolly Varden trout**, a gorgeous and hard-fighting

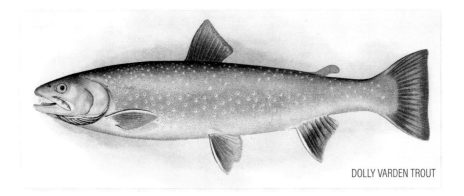

DOLLY VARDEN TROUT

member of the char family. The opportunity to tussle with a few of them couldn't be passed up.

Four of us got in the dinghy with our fishing tackle, with general directions to likely haunts for the Dolly Varden and headed off on a more immersive adventure. Remember, this was not a theme park or a guide-led expedition. We were on our own, and while all fairly seasoned outdoorsmen, there would be no protective glass or railings between us and nature. If we were to revel in the bounty of these exotic fish, then any dangers waiting out there would have to be addressed on their own terms and turf.

While searching for those beautiful trout, our presence also drew in some native and untamed Kodiak bears. From the deck of our "mothership," the bears had been gorgeous spectacles that we could literally watch for hours as they frolicked, fished, and sat around. They weren't cute and cuddly teddy bears, but they were beautiful nonetheless—at a distance. Up close, my feelings were a bit more mixed. Respectful of their territory, but aware that we both wanted the same fish, I still valued my life over theirs and hoped, in the best-case scenario, that we'd have no interactions on foot.

When we got to the prime fishing grounds, we were not surprised to see several bears who shared our fishing intentions. They were feeding on trout and salmon, and while aware of our presence, they really weren't interested in us at all.

We hiked in about four miles to a scenic and very "fishy" looking pool that provided prime casting angles and access to the water without spooking the fish. Like the bears, the trout may never have seen humans before, but their natural instincts would put them on guard if they encountered anything out of the ordinary. We tried to minimize our presence and perceived threat.

The fishing, as promised, was exceptional. Cast after cast, we hooked and landed wild trout that likely had never seen a lure before. They glistened with bright colors and swam away as we released them, clearly no worse for wear. Then we'd fire in another cast and do it all over again. Our only limitation was time.

As the clock ticked toward dark, we headed back out on the same path we'd safely used before. Only one problem—the bears that had been innocently feeding in the river were now basking on shore. Some were napping off the big feed, but others stood sentry, guarding over the group. We were alerted to their presence even before we could see them, as massive tracks and "scat" now littered the trail.

We continued walking—after all, we had to get back—but now with our senses heightened.

In the water, there was a bear cub enjoying a full belly, the cool stream, and the diminishing daylight. Up above, on a sheer cliff, sat mama bear watching intently. We knew that the first rule of the Alaskan bush is to never get between a mama bear and her cub, no matter how easy your passage might seem, or how difficult her path to the cub might be. Our trail went directly under the cliff, on the side of the stream where the cub stood. The **"fight-or-flight"** instinct told us that a swift jog between them might get us back safely, but everything we had been taught told us to wait it out.

So, we waited.

And waited.

And waited.

It was probably 30 minutes, but it seemed like hours. Our stomachs were growling. We were growing impatient. We started to question the decision to leave the bigger boat on our own. Calmer heads needed to prevail.

The four of us sat there stoically and tried to figure out what to do. Above everything, we all agreed that under no circumstances would we take off running. The "flight" portion of our instincts was the one most likely to lead to a bad outcome. Still, we had to do *something*. We collectively decided to try walking out—between mama and cub—in a single-file line, quietly and nonthreateningly, yet with deliberate speed.

I had been entrusted with a twelve-gauge shotgun and took that responsibility seriously. I stayed back and allowed the first member of our group to proceed in front of me, watching carefully. As he got between mama bear and cub, the mama started making her way down toward the water and was almost to our level in no time at all. For a large and seemingly clumsy animal, Kodiak bears are remarkably fast

on flat ground, with the speed of Olympic sprinters. There was no way we'd all be able to get past without a fight once she was at our level.

My friend in front did what came naturally and took off to safety. The two friends behind me suddenly got wheels and bumped me from behind. So much for our agreement not to take off running under any circumstances. These three intelligent, sophisticated, thoughtful, and caring friends—none of whom would hurt a fly—have all made high-pressure decisions affecting hundreds of people in their personal and professional lives. They didn't plan to run. They didn't expect to run. Nevertheless, when their caveman instincts kicked in from the stressful situation, they all ran. In hindsight I don't blame them, but at the time it was incredibly frustrating and potentially quite dangerous for us all.

I'm not patting myself on the back unnecessarily for my restraint, as I was the only one with a firearm, but I did not run.

The bear was getting closer. And closer. And closer.

What might have seemed like a human-sized animal from the larger boat had morphed into an absolutely giant prehistoric beast as it approached me. I could see her hair standing up, individual teeth, and the fire in her eyes. This was not a friendly visit. She was going to do whatever it took to protect her baby.

If the visual stimuli weren't terrifying enough, she started to roar. This was no simple yell or attempt to scare me off—she was warning the whole massive state of Alaska that someone was in *her* territory, against *her* will, trying to kill *her* most precious baby. It was more deafening than any rock concert or sporting event. I could feel it in my skin and bones and it took me out of the 21st century, back to primordial days thousands of years ago. Fight or flight seemed to be my best—and only—choice.

By the time she was within ten yards of me, I had the shotgun off my back, out in front of me, and perched on my shoulder. The noise was deafening. She was foaming at the mouth and looked even bigger than a few seconds earlier. There was simply no way to outrun her or beat her mano-a-mano. At the same time, I really didn't want to shoot if I didn't have to do so, because if I missed, or didn't kill her, she was going to come at me with an even greater head of steam. Pulling the trigger would mean her or me. One or the other—but not both.

At that point, I issued this ultimatum: "If she takes one more step, I'm firing," because that would give the chance to get at least two rounds off, enough to stun her if they didn't kill her.

I don't know what went through her mind, but at that point she must've felt that she'd exercised her maternal powers.

She never took another step forward.

I never had to fire.

I stood there, literally shaking in my boots, trying not to let my face betray any level of fear, because if it did, she might change her mind, change her course, and start coming at me again.

I backed away, neither fighting nor fleeing in the panic-stricken sense of the word. I never took my eyes off her, either, and kept backing away until far out of the direct path between the two bears. Only at that point did the emotion truly flow through me. All the way back to the boat, and probably for hours thereafter, I was rattled. Telling the story today puts me back in that frame of mind.

Am I sorry I went on that fishing expedition?

Absolutely not, because not only did I experience angling nirvana, but I faced down fear to get it. It was the only time in my fifty-plus years on Earth that my life was truly threatened, and I came through unscathed.

You can't go back in time and change your behavior, so I'll never know what would have happened if I'd run or fired the shotgun. The past is past—and it is, of course, prologue as well. I faced my fear, and I'm stronger because of it. I intuitively and intellectually channeled the information at my disposal and came out of it clean. We all did. Now I use that knowledge and experience to confront whatever fears I might have about the future. Having faced down the bear unscathed, I'm far less scared and far more excited about future confrontations than I otherwise might be.

Do blockchain, artificial intelligence, and other developments faze me? Absolutely not. I'm ready to take them on and to go on another amazing "fishing trip of a lifetime."

What I learned from the bear encounter is that fear is real. **Fear releases the adrenaline hormone**, which comes from the hypothalamus and causes our hearts to beat faster and our lungs to breathe deeper. Fear also releases the hormone cortisol, which increases blood sugar levels by converting stored glycogen and fats into blood sugar. It also suppresses the immune response and inflammation. Fear is a real chemical reaction.

Fear is the #1 obstacle people face when trying to be transparent. Going back a hundred years, a thousand years, or ten-thousand years, humans survived by camouflaging, hiding, and masking from predators and other humans. That was survival. Today we are being asked instead to provide full transparency, to do something that one-hundred years ago would have ended our fate. That's a hard reversal to engineer.

The good news is that people can adapt and change very quickly. The next time you're trying to be transparent and fear takes over, know that this is normal. Know that you can overcome those fears. You have done it before and can do it again. This is another reason for the 6Ts of Exponential Transparency: to make it ridiculously simple and easy for any person, company, or government to overcome the fears of being transparent.

TRANSPARENCY CHANGES EVERYTHING !!

PERSPECTIVES

CHAPTER 12 | FACING FEAR

a·dren·al·ine

/ə'dren(ə)lən/

a hormone secreted by the adrenal glands, especially in conditions of stress, increasing rates of blood circulation, breathing, and carbohydrate metabolism and preparing muscles for exertion.

THE PAST IS PAST—
AND IT IS, OF COURSE,
PROLOGUE AS WELL.

TRANSPARENCY WAVE

WHY **IT MATTERS:**

- We can fully expect to live longer than prior generations, to enjoy greater prosperity, comfort, and luxury, and to shape our future through transparency.

- Fear is the #1 obstacle people face when trying to be transparent.

ADVICE:

- Face your fears head on.

- Overcoming your fears will unleash your greatest opportunities.

TAKE**AWAYS:**

- Fight-or-flight is a natural human reaction.

- Fear is a chemical reaction. It is real, but it can be overcome.

ACTION STEPS:

- To help overcome your fears, follow the 6Ts of Exponential Transparency—Transparency Standards, Terms, Total Accountability, Transparent Cost, Truth and Trust.

- Adapt and change.

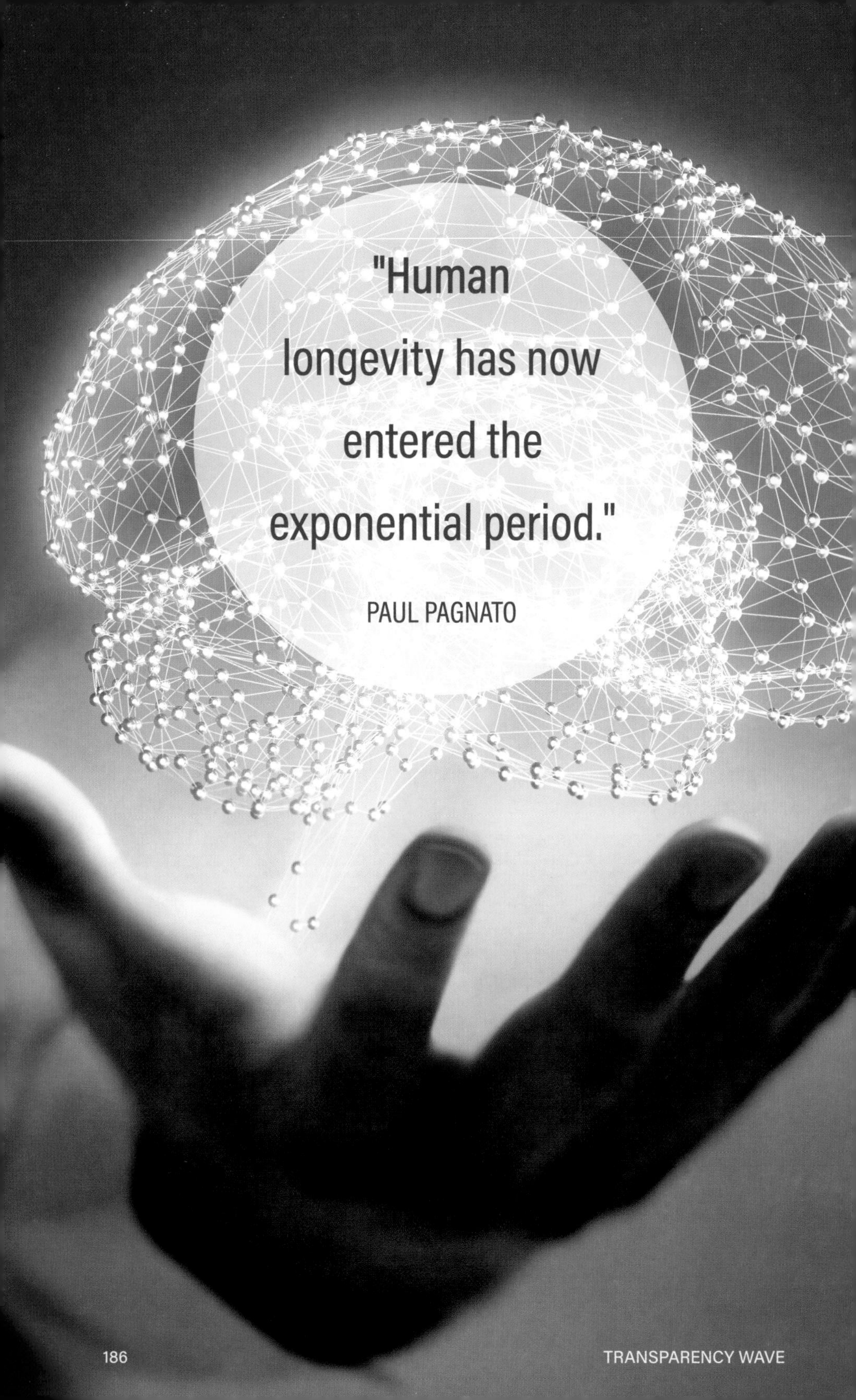

"Human
longevity has now
entered the
exponential period."

PAUL PAGNATO

CHAPTER 13

Longevity and Opportunities

Life expectancy was linear for over 100,000 years, but in the last hundred years, it has increased by 30 years. The average lifespan for a human in its earliest stages was eighteen years. During the Roman Empire, this ticked up to 22 and has been expanding ever so slowly until the last century when it entered the exponential period. The cover of *TIME* magazine featured a picture of a baby with the caption: "This baby could live to be 142 years old."[1]

Jeanne Louise Calment of France was the longest-living human in recorded history. She lived from 1875 to 1997, an astonishing 122 years. Ms. Calment was known for being **immune to stress, never letting anything bother her**. There must be something to the cliché, "Don't sweat the small stuff." Mayo Clinic research has shown that meditating for only ten minutes a day can decrease one's

Will this baby live to **142**?

Jeanne Louise Calment, The Longest Living Human in Recorded History

stress level. The benefits include reduced anxiety, depression, blood pressure, cardiovascular disease, and tension headaches. Anyone can do anything for ten minutes! Ms. Calment also fasted daily and never ate breakfast. She consumed a weekly average of two pounds of unprocessed chocolate (cacao beans). All of us can learn a lot from my hero Jeanne Louise Calment.

Longevity is now significantly impacting most industries, from health care to insurance to our Social Security program. In the wealth management space, advisors need to properly service individuals spanning three, four, or even five generations. PagnatoKarp serves clients across multiple generations whose needs and preferences vary greatly. Individuals from the **Greatest Generation (age 92+)** prefer personalized service, while those from the **Baby Boomer generation (age 54 to 72)** prefer both personal and technology-based services, and the **Millennials and Gen Z (age 17 to 37)** prefer a focus on technology with a light personal touch. The amount of savings needed for someone to live to 80 is very different than those required to thrive until 100. Financial planners need to now account for an additional 20+ years.

Dr. Laura Carstensen is the founding director of the Stanford Center for Longevity and the principal investigator for the Stanford Life Span Development Laboratory, one of the first and most prestigious academic centers studying longevity. The center's research has found that individuals living a long life can be broadly segmented into **three pillars: financial, social engagement, and mobility**. Remarkably, the first two pillars are centered around one's financial well-being. Studies show that humans are more socially engaged when financially stable.

Where Dr. Carstensen's work intersects with mine most closely is in the field of financial planning. If you're going to live to be 120, with your physical body and mental health in good order for most of that time, you'll need to be financially sound. Part of planning for that is the magic of compound interest (at this point in the book, can you tell that I think it's super, super important?). The other part involves reimagining the progression of life.

Even in this era of great prosperity, the model for most Americans is to retire in their early 60's, needing their Social Security payments to survive, yet not maximizing their benefits because their primary goal is to get out of the workforce as soon as possible. That simply will not be productive or sustainable going forward, said Dr. Carstensen.

"Longevity will change every aspect of our lives," says Dr. Carstensen. "Work life, especially, needs to change. Currently, people work way too hard in the middle of life and not enough in their late 60's, 70's, and 80's. Individuals are exhausted, and societies are losing the contributions of older people due to messages that they're no longer needed. The most compelling reason we need to change is that the existing model doesn't work."

"WE END UP WITH A WHOLE POPULATION OF PEOPLE FROM SIXTY-SEVEN ON UP WHO ARE TALENTED AND HEALTHY AND ABLE TO CONTRIBUTE, BUT **THEY'RE NO LONGER CONTRIBUTING.**"

DR. LAURA CARSTENSEN
STANFORD CENTER FOR LONGEVITY

LIFE EXPECTANCY
FROM THE BRONZE AGE TO THE 21ST CENTURY

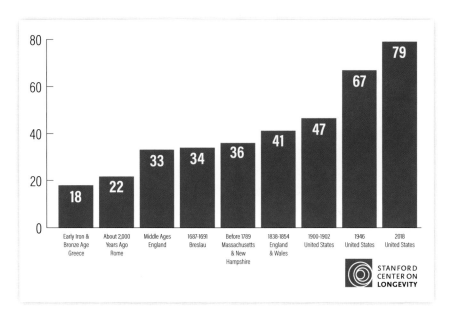

18	22	33	34	36	41	47	67	79
Early Iron & Bronze Age Greece	About 2,000 Years Ago Rome	Middle Ages England	1687-1691 Breslau	Before 1789 Massachusetts & New Hampshire	1838-1854 England & Wales	1900-1902 United States	1946 United States	2018 United States

STANFORD CENTER ON LONGEVITY

Longer life and changing life priorities will require a new outlook, and this has to be enforced by a combination of market forces, regulatory and legal advances, and a changing societal understanding of what's important.

"Longer lives afford us the opportunity to improve quality of life all the way through," Dr. Carstensen continued. "We can work shorter work weeks but more years. Fathers and mothers can spend more time with young children, postponing intense work to years when the children are grown. I am sometimes asked: 'That sounds great, but am I going to be able to get back in the workforce when I'm 40? And if I can't, then I've really made a very bad decision.' So, I think we need to do a lot of things. I think policy changes would be great if people could get access to some kind of support during times when they're working less than full-time."

"Societies that invest in citizens' capabilities for the long run will have great advantages," she continued. "I hold financial services up as the industry that—more than any other industry—can help us make the kinds of changes we need. Products that allow portable savings can help people move in and out of the workforce. We can take risks when we're young and know that we'll be okay when we are older. I think we need new savings models and plans. And I think that we need to make them available not just for the wealthy, but more importantly, we need to make them available to people who don't have a lot of resources."

Aging is not a steady downhill slide. To the extent that it ever was, or is, we're reducing the steepness and speed at which it progresses, but that requires some input from each person. As increasingly individual information is available, and it is less averaged or amalgamated, we can modify our lifestyles, stay involved with our communities and families, and engage in the health and financial practices likely to benefit each of us the most.

TRANSPARENCY CHANGES EVERYTHING !!

MEDITATION
500M GLOBAL
10% US

LONGEVITY IN A MULTI-FAMILY OFFICE

Generation	Age	Nickname	Traits
1	92+	The Greatest Generation	• Assertive and energetic doers • Community-minder • Strong sense of personal civic duty • Marriage is for life • Strong loyalty • Debt averse • Grew up without modern conveniences (refrigerators, electricity, A/C)
2	73-91	Mature/Silents	• Korean and Vietnam War generation • Pre-feminism women • Loyal to employer • Richest, most free-spending retirees in history • Marriage is for life • Avid readers, especially newspapers • Disciplined, self-sacrificing, cautious
3	54-72	Baby Boomers	• The "Me" generation – self-righteous and self-centered • Buy it now and use credit • 1st generation to raise children in two-income household • 1st divorce generation • Optimistic, driven, team-oriented • Envision technology and innovation as learning process • More positive about authority, hierarchy, tradition

Generation	Age	Nickname	Traits
4	38-53	Generation X	· "Latch key kids" · Entrepreneurial, individualistic, suspicious of organization · Want to save the neighborhood, not the world · Desire a chance to learn, explore, make a contribution · Into labels and brand names · Want what they want, and want it now – credit card debt · Cautious, skeptical, self-reliant
5	18-37	Generation Y (Millennium)	· Respect authority, optimistic, focused · Schedule everything · Feel enormous academic pressure · Digitally literate – get most information from internet · Assertive with strong views (unlimited access to information) · Want fast and immediate processing · Do not live to work
6	<17	Generation Z (Boomlets)	· Eco-fatigue – tired of hearing about the environment · Savvy consumers – know what they want and how to get it · Oversaturated with brands · Have never known a world without computers and cell phones · In 2006 there were a record # of births – 49% were Hispanic

op·por·tu·ni·ty

/äpər't(y)o'onədē/

a set of circumstances that makes it
possible to do something.

NEW LIFE CYCLE

EDUCATION SCIENTIST LEISURE

START BUSINESS  DREAM JOB WORK BACK TO SCHOOL

PagnatoKarp

LEISURE WORK **TrueFiduciary®** GIVING BACK FEELING GREAT !!

WHY **IT MATTERS:**

- Following a few basic longevity principles will increase your life expectancy by decades.

ADVICE:

- Don't sweat the small stuff—stress leads to accelerated aging.

- Living a longer life requires more savings—start early and save aggressively. Let compound interest work for you.

- Follow Jeanne Louise Calment's recipe for longevity— be immune to stress and consume lots of cacao.

TAKE**AWAYS:**

- The three pillars of longevity are:
  Financial—the average person makes thirteen financial decisions every day. Being financially stable decreases the stress of these decisions.

  Social engagement—people not financially stable withdraw socially, fearing not being able to financially participate with friends' social activities.

  Mobility—we only need ten minutes of an elevated heart rate per day. That's like taking a fast walk for ten minutes.

- The cycle of life now has people working longer and having multiple careers.

ACTION STEPS:

- Consider meditating for ten minutes a day. Meditation has proven to reduce stress and increase one's IQ.

- Live within your means—save at least 15% of your pre-tax income each year.

"TRANSPARENCY WILL LEAD TO AN ABUNDANCE OF MEDICAL INNOVATIONS."

PETER DIAMANDIS

CHAPTER 14

Keeping the Mind Fresh

Although still in my 50's, I work diligently to stay healthy and hope to be less than halfway through my life. I eat carefully, exercise and meditate regularly, seek both preventive and curative medical care, and take time off to rejuvenate.

To live past the century mark—and I certainly intend to—means ensuring that not only are my expected number of years growing, but my overall quality of life is improving. Obviously, I want to avoid any aches, pains, and more serious physical problems, but the mental side of things is every bit as important. Just about all of us have had to deal with saying "goodbye" to a relative who suffered from Alzheimer's, or some other form of dementia, and was gone before they were officially deceased.

No one wants to live in a vegetative or functionally vegetative state. At the same time, we are loath to admit that forgetting where we put our keys, or the time of our dinner reservation, is the sign of something more meaningful. We chalk it up to "having too much on our minds" or old age, or both.

That's a shame, because there are things we can do to postpone or even reverse the advancement of these maladies and conditions. The state of mental health and dementia research and treatment is far further along than it was 30 years, 20 years, or even a decade ago, but you have to face things head on to treat them.

Fortunately, there's an increasing level of transparency in this arena, too, and once again it's Millennials who are leading the way—putting their trust with those organizations that operate transparently in cost, accountability, truth, and the 6Ts of Exponential Transparency. **"The Millennials are growing up at a time when information is everything and it's immediately accessible,"** said Dr. Lisa Genova, a Harvard-trained PhD in neuroscience who is perhaps better known as a novelist who often tells tales that involve neurological disorders. They ask, **"Why wouldn't I want to know everything I can about what's in my body?"**

Historically, that hasn't been the case. Diseases—whether it's Alzheimer's, HIV, Huntington's, or breast cancer, to name a few—carried with them either real or perceived stigmas and burdens beyond their medical scope. Dr. Genova recalled that, in her parents' generation, people called cancer "The Big C."

"Fifty years ago, no one would even mention the word," Dr. Genova said. "They'd whisper about it. That person with cancer really went

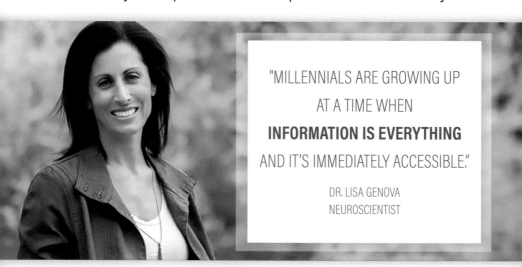

"MILLENNIALS ARE GROWING UP AT A TIME WHEN **INFORMATION IS EVERYTHING** AND IT'S IMMEDIATELY ACCESSIBLE."

DR. LISA GENOVA
NEUROSCIENTIST

through that experience by themselves in the house unseen, unheard, lots of shame and stigma with alienation and isolation."

As cancer unfortunately became more mainstream and less stigmatized, that isolation did not lift so readily from Alzheimer's patients and their families.

"No one wanted to admit that you or your husband had Alzheimer's," Dr. Genova continued. "You weren't going to tell people because you were embarrassed and kept it to yourself. People went through that experience alone, and no one shared how to get through something like this."

Rather than turning outward, engaging transparently and crowdsourcing information and coping strategies, the "fear factor" led people inward. Even if they weren't putting their heads in the sand, they nevertheless didn't go outside of their circles for understanding and assistance. That didn't help those suffering—either themselves or their family members—nor did it provide a baseline of understanding for the next family to be victimized.

"The older folks are used to not discussing Alzheimer's," Dr. Genova added. "They were just going to keep it to themselves. Very private about it, whereas I think people who are my age, we sort of dragged it out of the closet and made it a topic that we can have a conversation about. That's what happened with cancer, right? We wear looped ribbons and bake casseroles and have meal trains and we do the walks. We rally around our family, friends, and neighbors who have cancer—and what changed is we began talking about it. Conversation fuels social change. So, people started talking about Alzheimer's—that's a new thing. I think people who discuss it are in their 40s and 50s—people looking to prevention as a way to fight this disease."

What's the result of all of this?

In effect, it marries the best attributes of both high-tech and low-tech connection to other people. On the high-tech front, we're now out there seeking solutions from the scientific community and creating data for them, both before we develop the disease and in the midst of the fight. On the low-tech side of things, normalizing discussions about Alzheimer's has reduced the shame associated with the disease and enhanced community-building efforts. For example, if you are less inhibited about telling your friends and neighbors that a family member has the disease, they can provide assistance that de-stresses you. It might be as simple as asking them to look out for your father or grandfather if they see him walking in the neighborhood. It might be a night of "babysitting" or running an errand so that you don't have to leave your relatives alone.

NO MATTER WHAT THE LEVEL OF ASSISTANCE, TRANSPARENCY AND OPENNESS HAVE LED TO OUTCOMES WHERE WE'RE NO LONGER SELF-MADE PARIAHS.

"There can be a sense of connection, whereas before there was total disconnection," Dr. Genova said. "In the closet we can't talk, and nobody benefits. Still, for older folks who grew up in a time when it was in the closet, it's a little harder for them to change that mindset." Transparency changes this.

The intersection of advanced research, genomics, and transparency about Alzheimer's (and conditions like Alzheimer's) has led to an exponential growth in our ability to slow it down and deal with it. There remains no cure for the disease, and indeed it cannot be diagnosed in humans until it is very much advanced. Nevertheless, we are getting closer to be able to mute its effects and to analyze who is most likely to develop some sort of dementia—which is half the battle in terms of treating its most odious symptoms and problems.

Part of the advances are from information that was once "blurry" that is now exceptionally clear. As Raymond McCauley—scientist, engineer and entrepreneur working at the forefront of biotechnology—stated, "We're reading DNA like code."

It is my belief that even if doctors (or doctors aided by the benefits of artificial intelligence) don't find a cure for Alzheimer's within my lifetime, they will nevertheless be able to predict who will get it based on a combination of genetics, genomics, and other more objective tests. When that happens, I will be first in line to find out whatever I can about my own condition. Indeed, my wife and I have already undertaken "virtual physicals," including complete body scans, to search for signs of any preventable or treatable maladies anywhere in our bodies. There are various other diseases that may not be curable or fully preventable, but which can be slowed or attacked if found early. Examples that come to mind include breast cancer and Huntington's Disease.

Part of spreading the word requires cultural changes to the medical profession. As Dr. Genova said:

"**Something like 45% of people who should have a diagnosis of Alzheimer's aren't actually even told they have it by their physicians** because the physicians are afraid it will be too stressful and upsetting for them to hear the word 'Alzheimer's.' Can you imagine if you had cancer and your doctors refused to even tell you because they thought it would be upsetting? It's like, 'Why would I tell you that you have Alzheimer's when it's just going to depress you and there's nothing you can do about it?' Which is 100% not true. There's a lot you can do about it. If there's not a pill that will treat or cure it—and we don't really have that yet—is it fair to let you think about how this is going to affect your finances,

"WE'RE READING DNA LIKE CODE."

RAYMOND MCCAULEY
CHAIR OF DIGITAL BIOLOGY,
SINGULARITY UNIVERSITY

your future, your emotional system and psychological support, and the people who are going to need to be in place to care for you now or in five or ten years? And there's so much evidence now that clearly shows that lifestyle changes like eating a Mediterranean diet, aerobic exercise, getting enough quality sleep, staying cognitively and socially active, and lowering stress can all fight against the progression of Alzheimer's. So, I think a lack of transparency, at least in the relationship between physicians and their patients with Alzheimer's, is a real problem. There's just still so much fear and lack of communication between patient and doctor when it comes to this disease."

There's that word again: **Fear.**

Remember my story about the bear?

Consider Alzheimer's or cancer, or any one of a number of diseases, to be the bear in this context. When you're confronted face-to-face with a snarling beast, ruled by primitive emotions and an agenda of its own, there's no reasoning with it. Your choices get narrowed down to fight or flight—or standing your ground with the figurative "shotgun" and hoping for your best.

In either situation, though, none of us has the inclination to just lie down and give up. Or do we?

Historically, being diagnosed with cancer or dementia or some other stigmatized and arguably incurable disease led not only to social ostracization, but also to a host of other negative ramifications.

For example, generations ago, a person might have been fired for having one of these harsh diseases, even if they were still capably performing

---

HISTORICALLY, BEING DIAGNOSED WITH CANCER OR DEMENTIA OR SOME OTHER STIGMATIZED AND ARGUABLY INCURABLE DISEASE LED NOT ONLY TO SOCIAL OSTRACIZATION, BUT ALSO TO A HOST OF OTHER NEGATIVE RAMIFICATIONS.

their jobs. Family medical leave wasn't legally protected, and the Health Insurance Portability and Accountability Act (HIPAA) wasn't passed until 1996, so your secret—even if you were dealing with it head-on—wasn't necessarily your own.

Under the pre-protection environment, a person with a disease like HIV, even if they were doing nothing that made it risky or transmittable to coworkers, could be put in a position of further discomfort and mistreated based on that diagnosis. Sometimes the mistreatment wasn't overt—instead of being fired outright, the victim would be passed over for a promotion, a raise, or a bonus. That situation has less legal protection and, in any case, it's much harder to prove than a direct firing. Perhaps worst of all, at a time when the immune system or someone's mental health was most compromised, it piled onto the uncertainty and stress surrounding the given disease and its protocols.

Why would you want to find out what you have if the result will be further problems rather than a supportive interpersonal ecosystem?

Huntington's Disease has less of a widespread stigma than AIDS or Alzheimer's, perhaps only because it is lesser known, but it can be every bit as debilitating. Its progression is marked by the death of an increasing number of brain cells, resulting in mood swings, decreased cognitive ability, and lack of coordination. Ultimately it may lead to dementia or complete physical disability. Symptoms often start to arise in early middle age, as opposed to the typically later outward development of Alzheimer's. It is typically (but not always) inherited from one's parents, and there are increasingly powerful and effective medications that can greatly slow its progression (think of them as pharmaceutical "pepper spray," which would slow but not stop or kill the bear's progress, giving you just enough time to avoid the negative effects of the chase for a bit longer, if not escape).

Despite all that, Dr. Genova informed me that, "In the United States, 90% of the people who are at risk for Huntington's choose not to find out. And 75% of people in Canada who are at risk choose not to find out."

Why is that?

She believes that it's not just the outward stigma, the way that other people will treat us, but also how it will affect our own plans, moods, and activities. "It's a very gray area," she said. "Some people might not undertake the genetic testing because they think, for example, 'I'm planning to go to medical school and if I found I was gene positive, I might not go to medical school, and I really want to go.' Or 'if I find that I'm positive then I might not get married and have kids. And I deserve to get married and have kids because my parents got married and had me. If my mom had found out she had Huntington's, maybe she would never have had me, and I wouldn't be here. I'm 25 years old and my life is great and fun, and if I get Huntington's it might not be until I'm 50, so why do I have to know I'm going to get something when I'm 50? I could get cancer tomorrow.'"

"People go through all these rationalizations," she continued. "Reasonable or not, about why they just would prefer not to know."

Eventually, however, the opportunity to catch these diseases early—and treat them effectively even if we can't fully prevent or cure them—will outweigh any shame associated with their emergence or the fear of the negative psychological impacts that will accompany their diagnosis. We are on the cusp of that now as the result of the emergence of all sorts of exponential technologies. That's why this is an exciting time.

"It's happening exponentially," Dr. Genova declared. "It's not just neuroscience anymore—it's neuroscience and physics and big data. It might not be someone in neuroscience who discovers the cure for Alzheimer's. It might be an immunologist, someone in big data. It might be an imaging specialist. It's anybody's game, and it might be a collaboration between a bunch of disciplines. It's like your phone was in the year 2000 versus now. Think of how much your cell phone has changed and what you're able to do. Well, advancement in the research tools in neuroscience moved at a similar rate. We just weren't able to look at what caused Alzheimer's in 2000, and now we can. That's true of all diseases and everything in the body. We're going to see a lot of exciting things happening. It's going to be an entirely different world in the next 20 years in terms of what you worry about dying of, and what health looks like."

What if I told you a 13-year-old created the leading pancreatic cancer test? What if I told you he did all his research on Google? What if I told you his motivation was purpose-based versus profits?

His name is **Jack Andraka**, and he developed the leading patent-pending test for pancreatic cancer. Jack lost a close family friend to this cancer and learned that 85% of all pancreatic cancer cases were diagnosed late. Jack was on a mission to change this, and he is now on his way. This is a beautiful example of how some of the greatest innovations occur by people

SOURCE: Flickr: Visioneering 2013

with low levels of industry competence. They approach a problem from a different perspective.

But amid all this excitement, advancement, and possibility, there remain concerns that will require a functional shift in how we live. People who don't consider them, especially in the first long-lived generations, are going to struggle, but you don't have to.

As Dr. Genova put it so bluntly, "What the hell are we going to do when we all live to a hundred and beyond?"

"**In 1900, life expectancy was 47 in the United States,"** she explained. **"It's now 77 when you're born,** but if you make it to my age, I'm going to live hopefully to my 90s and beyond. So awesome! We've gained at least 30 years in longevity, but wait a minute: What do we do with those years? I don't think it follows the linear model we've been working in, which is you get educated, you get a job, you get married, you retire from your job, you die. What does this look like beyond 'retirement'? What can those years look like? I don't know, but we talk about this a lot. That's going to have to change. We can't just have a populous of millions and millions of people who are just watching TV and going to the mall for 40 years. And we need our brain span to match our lifespan."

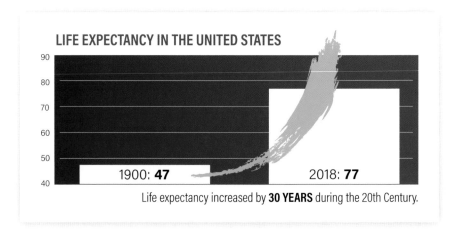

LIFE EXPECTANCY IN THE UNITED STATES

1900: **47**

2018: **77**

Life expectancy increased by **30 YEARS** during the 20th Century.

One of the thought leaders, whose work and expertise I've relied upon to consider the questions that Dr. Genova raised, is Dr. Laura Carstensen, whom I briefly introduced you to in Chapter 8. She's one of the most thoughtful and positive people I've known. Just talking with her gets me excited about the decades and centuries to come, and the changes that we're all likely to experience and benefit from. She's been published not just in scientific journals, but also in mainstream publications like *The New York Times* and *Time* magazine. In other words, like Dr. Genova, the neuroscientist-slash novelist, much of her work is accessible and digestible to anyone who is interested, literate, and has an open mind. I suppose that's why both have produced greatly respected and uber-popular TED Talks: what they're saying resonates. It helps us to understand a lot that would be otherwise uncertain. Perhaps most importantly, it gives us hope and reason to look forward to the future using what I perceive to be a PMA lens.

Dr. Carstensen, who has become a close personal friend as well as a muse and professional colleague, has allowed me to examine how we should consider and address the coalescing of our changing world and increasing longevity. I firmly believe that it can be a win-win situation, but there will be people who won't prepare properly. Part of my mission in life is to enable as many people as possible to gain all the benefits while suffering few or none of the downsides. The challenge, as she framed it, is to provide transparency in its optimized form:

"**I think the mission is to make the world more transparent to people so they can make better decisions**," Dr. Carstensen said. "It's basically knowing all the facts. I think we go through most of our lives relying on faith. We walk out the door, and we assume that when we take one step down there'll be ground beneath us. We're trusting a lot and sometimes that works for us. But then there are these decisions we make about our health and what really matters to us in terms of health and fitness."

"The financial services industry has helped people enormously over the last 30 years," Dr. Carstensen continued. "People have been asked to take responsibility for their own financial well-being and financial services is the only industry that's really helping on the one hand. On the other hand, there are all sorts of built-in obscure and elusive aspects to investing and saving that most people don't even know, so we're not making good decisions because we don't have all the information."

"On the downside," she continued, "I think we're also entering a time where there will be lots more transparency about all of us that we haven't agreed to. We're seeing that with young people and Facebook accounts, and we're being monitored by Google and Facebook and all sorts of businesses watching what we eat and what we buy and so on. So, there's also a transparency that's being imposed on us as individuals."

Dr. Carstensen cited the example of insurance companies that incentivize their enrollees or potential enrollees to **wear devices that give all kinds of information about their health and well-being in real-time**.

Who wouldn't want access to all of that?

Well, as we established when discussing Dr. Genova's work, above, historically many people have not wanted to know that information, but the tide is turning. Increasingly, we want to know what maladies we have or that we're likely to develop. Modern medicine allows us more and more ways to prevent, cure, or slow them down. There are still some headwinds against that trend, many of them generational, but the tide is turning. Now, it seems, the fear is not what we might know about ourselves, but rather what others might learn about us. "Others," in this case, don't necessarily mean our friends and neighbors and coworkers, but rather institutions in positions of power.

In other words, if your insurer can monitor you in real time, they might be able to reward you for not smoking or drinking. They might reduce your deductible because they can see that you exercise vigorously and effectively seven days a week. On the other hand, they might be inclined to deny a claim or deny coverage on some factor or action that seems irrelevant to you.

Even Dr. Carstensen, who is on the front lines of these issues and has spent countless hours considering, discussing, and writing about them, is a little nervous about where all the information could go. In describing a "fabulous study" being jointly conducted by Google and Stanford, one that she is certain "will lead to exponential advances in health," she said:

"I love it. I think it's fabulous, and I'm not joining it because I'm worried that the bad kind of information is going to get out somehow. It feels very invasive to me. Some of this is generational, but I don't feel like I have things to hide about myself or my activities. On the other hand, it feels like it's nobody's business, right? So, that's a part of it. Knowing how secure we can be with information, when we should worry, how do we get more information—all of those things are important."

IF YOUR INSURER CAN MONITOR YOU IN REAL-TIME, THEY MIGHT BE ABLE TO **REWARD YOU** FOR NOT SMOKING OR DRINKING. THEY MIGHT **REDUCE YOUR DEDUCTIBLE** BECAUSE THEY CAN SEE THAT YOU EXERCISE VIGOROUSLY AND EFFECTIVELY SEVEN DAYS A WEEK.

Dr. Carstensen recognizes that generations raised with Facebook/ Instagram/Snapchat might be less deterred by those concerns and added that socioeconomic factors might also play a role in citizens' openness to such information sharing. Nevertheless, like just about all the experts I consulted, she seemed to think that the key to crowdsourcing information and using it for good rather than purely self-interested purposes, will be to find "trusted sources."

"I don't think we can ask individuals to make those kinds of judgments on their own," Dr. Carstensen said. "It's impossible for individuals at a distance to make those judgments. But we need to find trusted sources that we can really count on, to be faithful to the consumer."

An epic example of this is the genomic test **23andMe**. Over **five million people** have used the genomic test and a stunning 80% of those users have opted to participate in the company's research. They have given permission for use of their DNA to help further genomic testing for other human beings. That is the essence of "seeking the flourishing of others." The FDA has already approved 23andMe to market tests that assess the genetic risks for ten significant health conditions. These include Parkinson's, Alzheimer's, and celiac disease.

That is much the same conclusion that Wyatt Andrews, the former National Correspondent for CBS News (who is quoted more extensively in Chapters 6 and 8) reached. He indicated that current market forces and political pressures have kept a great deal of news reporting segregated—and therefore the consumer who wants to sort out truth from fiction, or objectivity from subjectivity, has a massive and difficult undertaking ahead of them. Part of that may be resolved via the increased use of data and "news literacy." Remember the need to "train your algorithm"? Wyatt is convinced that there is currently little incentive for any partisan news source to lead you in that direction, especially because the need to do so depends on the individual holding a certain educational baseline.

Even if huge numbers of people "live in their own echo chambers" because they only consume news on Facebook where they get it for free, Andrews is hopeful that at some point we will be able "to educate the public about the downside of only consuming news via social media."

That's why he's hopeful. He believes that there can and will come a time when "honest brokers of the news [will] start winning in the marketplace."

"Somebody will figure out a way to monetize accurate reporting," Andrews said, "and at the level of watchdog investigative reporting that is required in our democracy to monitor the transgressions of everyone from dog catcher to president. To be clear, that's vital to our democracy and it's baked into the First Amendment of the Constitution that the dog catcher and the president, those guys should wake up every single day afraid of being embarrassed in the news media. **That line in the First Amendment of the Constitution by itself has helped make us one of the most productive, advanced societies in all of civilization.**"

Andrew's line about the need for and likelihood of an accurate news source reminded me of Marshall McLuhan's famous line that "the medium is the message," first published over fifty years ago in his book *Understanding Media: The Extensions of Man*. It allowed me to piece together how the disparate experts I've consulted have worked to express the positive side of futurism using different techniques. Dr. Lisa Genova, a highly-accredited and revered neuroscientist, has reached the greatest number of people, not by expressing her ideas in scientific papers, but rather by weaving them skillfully into novels. You have to meet your audience where they live and where they are best able to integrate the message into their own lives. It's why I'm excited about this book—oftentimes in meetings we pore over financial minutiae or evaluate complex investment structures in detail. That's important but putting these concepts into layman's terms—and by no means writing down to any audience—new audiences and greater numbers of people can be affected. That's remarkably empowering.

It's also why I'm excited about the Transparency Wave and exponential technological advances that continue to wow us every day. In the related fields of health and longevity, they will become more predictive, more accurate, and less invasive. As I said back in Chapter 8, when they get those microsensor tattoos ready to go, sign me up—despite my generational aversion to the idea of altering my body in that way.

TRANSPARENCY CHANGES EVERYTHING !!

con·ver·sa·tion

/känvər'sāSH(ə)n/

a talk, especially an informal one,
between two or more people, in which
news and ideas are exchanged.

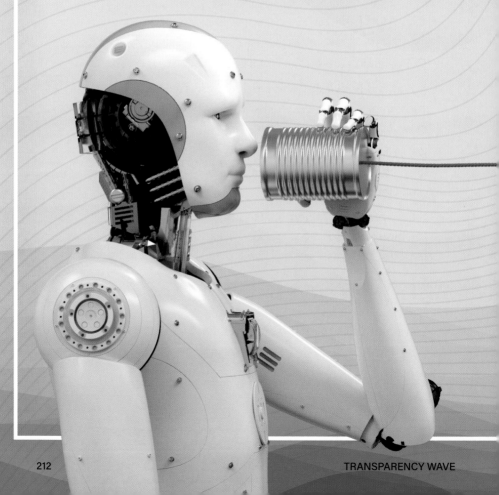

WHY **IT MATTERS:**

- Neuroscience, physics, and big data are exponentially changing the way diseases like Alzheimer's and dementia are treated.

ADVICE:

- Provide and seek transparency when diagnosed with a disease. This will help reduce stress and increase the probability of the best possible outcomes.

- Transparency regarding your health may have a greater impact on your loved ones than on yourself.

TAKE**AWAYS:**

- Conversation fuels social change.

- Advanced research, genomics, and transparency about Alzheimer's have led to an exponential growth in our ability to slow it down and deal with it.

- 45% of people who should be given a diagnosis of Alzheimer's aren't told they have it by their physicians, according to Dr. Lisa Genova.

- If a 13-year-old created the leading pancreatic cancer test, just imagine what solutions data scientists, artificial intelligence experts, and geneticists will discover in the next five years.

ACTION STEPS**:**

- Have a positive mental attitude toward longevity.

- Create a few new positive habits to help lead to substantial transformations in your mental health outcomes.

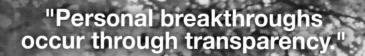

"Personal breakthroughs occur through transparency."

— Paul Pagnato —

CHAPTER 15

Longevity Demands a Plan

Is there an absolute ceiling on the number of years that a human being can live?

If so, what is it and how close can we get to it?

If not, what steps can we take to overcome perceived barriers?

If not, how can we ensure that once we overcome those barriers that we maintain quality of life?

There is no widespread consensus within the scientific community about the answers to these questions. Indeed, even in this era of exponential technological advances, we are still trying to answer questions that have bedeviled mankind since the beginning of time. Nearly all of us have the Ponce de Leon instinct to search for the fountain of youth. Some people find it and live active, vibrant lives into their 80's, 90's, and beyond. Others seem to prematurely age and give up on the search for eternal vitality, assuming that their outcomes are predetermined and that there's nothing they can do to change their own in any meaningful way.

> SINCE THE BEGINNING OF HUMAN EXISTENCE,
>
> **MANKIND HAS TRIED TO EXTEND OUR LIFESPANS.**

If your grandfather died at 40, and your father died at 40, it's easy to presume that you are destined for the same fate, no matter how you act or conduct your life. Conversely, if grandpa smoked a cigar every day, drank copious amounts of beer, never exercised, and still lived to be 102—dancing the tango until his final day—you might assume you don't need to take care of your health to live a long time. Those assumptions will change your behavior, often not for the better, and they may be based on a false premise. Indeed, some studies indicate that your lifespan is only 12% to 25% heritable.[1]

That means that you have control over 75% to 88% of your longevity "diagnosis."

Does that change the way you act?

If you're in the "likely to die by 40" demographic or the "likely to live past one-hundred" cohort, does that statistic change your behavior? Maybe previous generations died at 40 not because they were genetically predisposed to do so, but rather because they engaged in years of backbreaking labor in a soot- and carcinogen-filled coal mine. You work in a climate-controlled office. That's not necessarily a dispositive distinguishing factor, but it might be. If you ignore it and operate under the mantra of "live fast, die young, leave a good-looking corpse," you could very well end up a shocked and impoverished 80-year-old retiree.

As Edd Gent, a Singularity University writer who frequently discusses the intersection of engineering, computing, and biology put it: "Eternal life is no good without eternal youth." That extends not only to health outcomes, but also to positive financial consequences.

Since the beginning of human existence, mankind has tried to extend lifespans and improve the overall quality of the ensuing years, even if we couldn't quite articulate those intersecting goals. For the most part, that has led to linear improvements and increases. We've been able to cure some diseases and stave off the effects of others, yet there has not been a marked jump at any point in life expectancy.

We are now on the verge of seeing that jump, and it's largely the result of artificial intelligence. As Peter Diamandis wrote, in the very near future "Machine learning [will help us] to accomplish with 50 people what the pharmaceutical industry can barely do with an army of 5,000."

To date, pharmaceutical developments, medical advances, and research have been driven largely by short-term market forces. With the increased "manpower" of artificial intelligence, however, that convergence (as described by Diamandis) will result in "massive datasets in everything from gene expression to blood tests." This in turn means that "**novel drug discovery is about to get more than 100x cheaper, faster, and more intelligently targeted** and will soon enable extraordinary strides in longevity and disease prevention."

If we accept that the life expectancy of a middle-class American is somewhere in the range of 80-years, adjusting for various factors, what is the ceiling for raising that number?

Jeanne Louise Calment of France passed away in 1997 at 122 years old. That's 20-plus years ago; with today's advanced medical and preventive developments, there's a good chance that her outer limit might've been much higher. Indeed, there have been at least 40 people who exceeded

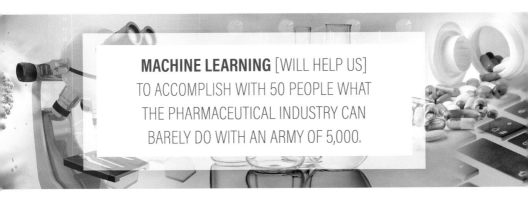

MACHINE LEARNING [WILL HELP US] TO ACCOMPLISH WITH 50 PEOPLE WHAT THE PHARMACEUTICAL INDUSTRY CAN BARELY DO WITH AN ARMY OF 5,000.

the age of 115 when they died[2]—that's a verified total, so there could be many more.

When you see that Calment was from Europe, or that the oldest living person at the time I'm writing this—Kane Tanaka (116+) is from Japan, you might assume that there is something about a European/Mediterranean or Japanese diet and lifestyle that promotes longevity. Maybe it's the salt air or the seafood diet. Perhaps it's the residue of some cultural distinction. But if you look down the list of the verified oldest people, it quickly becomes clear that might not be the case. Indeed, three of the top nine are from Japan, which would seem to support that thesis, but five of the top 15 and seven of the top 20 are from the United States. Certainly, you can assume that there's some reporting biases in that list. After all, if there's a random group of remote third-world villages where extreme longevity exists, it might not be reported.

Nevertheless, while it may seem that in the developed world there is no rhyme or reason to which countries produce the most consistently long-lived citizens, adjusting for a control group, there are certain pockets that consistently produce centenarians:[3]

THE FIVE BLUE ZONES

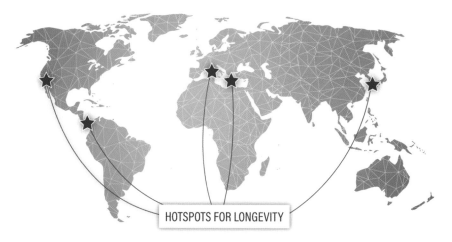

HOTSPOTS FOR LONGEVITY

Barbagia region of Sardinia, Italy—Mountainous highlands of inner Sardinia with the world's highest concentration of male centenarians.

Ikaria, Greece—Aegean Island with one of the world's lowest rates of middle age mortality and the lowest rates of dementia.

Nicoya Peninsula, Costa Rica—World's lowest rates of middle age mortality and second highest concentration of male centenarians.

Seventh Day Adventists—Highest concentration is around Loma Linda, CA. They live ten years longer than their North American counterparts.

Okinawa, Japan—Females over seventy are the longest-lived population in the world.

9 COMMON TRAITS OF **CENTENARIANS**

Author Dan Buettner, a National Geographic fellow and award-winning journalist, described the nine things that these groups in the **blue zones—the areas where people live the longest, healthiest lives—** have in common:[4]

1. MOVE NATURALLY

The world's longest-lived people don't pump iron, run marathons, or join gyms. Instead, they live in environments that constantly nudge them into moving without thinking about it. They grow gardens and don't have mechanical conveniences for house and yard work.

2. PURPOSE

The Okinawans call it "Ikigai" and the Nicoyans call it "plan de vida;" for both, it translates to "why I wake up in the morning." Knowing your sense of purpose is worth up to seven years of extra life expectancy.

3. DOWNSHIFT

Even people in the blue zones experience stress. Stress leads to chronic inflammation, associated with every major age-related disease. What the world's longest-lived people have that we don't are routines to shed that stress. Okinawans take a few moments each day to remember their ancestors, Adventists pray, Ikarians take a nap, and Sardinians do happy hour.

4. 80% RULE

"Hara hachi bu"—the Okinawan, 2,500-year-old Confucian mantra said before meals reminds them to stop eating when their stomachs are 80% full. The 20% gap between not being hungry and feeling full could be the difference between losing weight or gaining it. People in the blue zones eat their smallest meal in the late afternoon or early evening and then they don't eat any more the rest of the day.

5. PLANT SLANT

Beans, including fava, black, soy, and lentils, are the cornerstone of most centenarian diets. Meat—mostly pork—is eaten on average only five times per month. Serving sizes are three to four ounces, about the size of a deck of cards.

6. WINE AT 5

People in all blue zones (except Adventists) drink alcohol moderately and regularly. Moderate drinkers outlive non-drinkers. The trick is to drink one to two glasses per day (preferably Sardinian Cannonau wine), with friends and/or with food. And no, you can't save up all weekend and have 14 drinks on Saturday.

7. BELONG

All but five of the 263 centenarians belonged to some faith-based community. Denomination doesn't seem to matter. Research shows that attending faith-based services four times per month will add four to 14 years of life expectancy.

8. LOVED ONES FIRST

Successful centenarians in the blue zones put their families first. This means keeping aging parents and grandparents nearby or in the home (it lowers disease and mortality rates of children in the home too). They commit to a life partner (which can add up to three years of life expectancy) and invest in their children with time and love (they'll be more likely to care for you when the time comes).

9. RIGHT TRIBE

The world's longest-lived people chose—or were born into—social circles that supported healthy behaviors. Okinawans created "moais," groups of five friends that committed to each other for life. Research from the Framingham Studies shows that smoking, obesity, happiness, and even loneliness is contagious. The social networks of long-lived people have favorably shaped their health behaviors.

There might not be consensus on how long we can live, but by adopting some of those behaviors—along with some others—we are more likely to get to our ceilings, if any exist. They depend in large part on our willingness to accept personal transparency—openness, authenticity, being real. It may well be uncomfortable at first, but if you're transparent with yourself, you can achieve great things. Transparency builds your character and integrity and helps you to be the best you can be.

Shelley Fan, a neuroscientist at the University of California, San Francisco, "**studies ways to make old brains young again**," according to her Singularity University bio. In a paper she published last year, she cited a study published in *Science* magazine that suggests that "humans are nowhere near our maximum lifespan—if such a limit exists at all."[5] Indeed, if we can find ways to bypass or overcome some of the hurdles that we face in terms of the most common diseases and causes of death, she believes that our life expectancy will increase substantially.

For example, she quoted Dr. James Vaupel as explaining that "Cancer is quite a common cause of death for people in their 70's, 80's, and 90's. But very few people die from cancer over 100."

IF YOU LIVE TO 105, YOUR CHANCES OF DYING IN A GIVEN YEAR ARE ROUGHLY 50/50, AND IT SEEMS TO STAY THAT WAY.

Extrapolating that information out even further, she seemed to imply that people pick up steam, or at least avoid the most opportunistic causes of death, if they get past a certain age barrier.

"**If you live to 105, your chances of dying in a given year are roughly 50/50, and it seems to stay that way,**" she wrote.

Nevertheless, Fan didn't suggest that it will be easy to get a larger number of people to the 50/50 point of 105. Indeed, she cited various studies, most notably one from a team led by Dr. Jan Vijg at the Albert Einstein College of Medicine, that showed that maximum lifespan rose from 110 to 115 from the 1970's to the 1990's but did not meaningfully increase again between 1995 and 2016, despite substantial improvements in medicine, medical care, and other preventive measures. To some, she said, this suggests a "death plateau" and possibly a "hard limit" on how long we can live.

Nevertheless, whether your age ceiling is 100, 120, or higher, one of the primary changes in how science in 2019 and beyond move you closer to that limit involves increasingly personalized care. A lot of that will be interpreted and implemented through increasingly advanced genomics, the branch of molecular biology concerned with the structure, function, evolution, and mapping of genomes. That discipline goes beyond genetics by looking at all your genes in a comprehensive fashion, thereby enabling scientists to analyze your brain and other complex systems in a revolutionary manner.

When genomics was in its infancy, it took **13 years and $2.7 billion to map a single genome**. Today you can pay $1,000 and have your entire sequence back in three months. In five years, you'll be able to get that same information instantly for the equivalent of less than $100.[6]

What does this do for you?

It enables each of us to understand our risks and to attack our problems in a highly tailored and increasingly certain manner. So, if, for example, you are one of the millions of people worldwide who are prone to suffer from breast cancer, or you are already saddled with the disease, if you're just depending on a cure, you're out of luck. At the time of this writing, there is none. At the same time, as the result of advanced genomics, your oncologists can attack *your* cancer with a treatment steeped in personalized immunology.[7]

If doctors ascertain that genomic information, and then combine it with advances in artificial intelligence, the benefits multiply substantially. Several companies are already taking advantage of this synergy for the good of society.

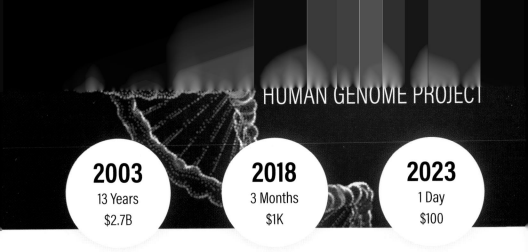

2003	2018	2023
13 Years	3 Months	1 Day
$2.7B	$1K	$100

Mitra Biotech, headquartered in Boston and with labs in Bangalore, India, for example, has devised a model that feeds a patient's tumor biopsies into a machine-learning algorithm to predict how she will respond to different drugs. BioNTech, based in Mainz, Germany, has developed several methods of immunotherapy treatments for cancer: protein coding and protein therapy, genetically engineered T cells, small molecule therapies, as well as a diagnostics platform that identifies the best treatment option for each patient. These approaches target the specific genome sequence of malignant tumors and, unlike chemo and radiation, they "can specifically kill cancer cells without as many side effects," says Dr. Ugur Sahin, cofounder and CEO of the firm. At the Mayo Clinic in Jacksonville, Florida a team is developing breast cancer and ovarian cancer vaccines aimed at stimulating the immune system right after tumors have been removed through surgery. And EpiVax Oncology in Rhode Island is crafting a precision vaccine that leverages the body's own immune system to attack and destroy cancer cells.[8]

Many of these advances in genomics and immunotherapy have been achieved—on an exponentially growing basis—over the past two decades, and particularly in the past few years. That corresponds with the rise in computing power (as Moore predicted) and, in turn, in artificial intelligence, as many of my mentors and role models not only predicted but also played an active role in changing.

The exciting things that are going on in the fields of health and longevity right now reflect the huge upside to these developments. I would be remiss, however, if I failed to acknowledge the downsides or obstacles that we must overcome.

The first set of obstacles relate to quality of life, as Edd Gent titled one of his Singularity University papers, "Eternal Life Is No Good Without Eternal Youth."[9] We might quibble with the semantics of that, noting that there are some benefits to maturity over the relative inexperience of youth, but Gent's point is well taken. If you are one of those people who "are clinging on past their shelf life," the prospect of enhanced or unlimited lifespans might not seem so appealing.

The two primary issues are **maintaining your physical well-being and your financial well-being into an advanced age**. No one wants to live a long life just for the sake of hitting a certain number. We want our years to be full and productive and enjoyable, each day an opportunity to achieve something. That's true not only for individuals, but for societies and the world as a whole. Imagine if all 90-year-olds, not just a small subgroup of them, remained lucid, motivated, and productive. That would increase the benefits to the world substantially, not just because they'd be productive, but also because they would bring a nonagenarian's valid and differentiated viewpoint to meaningful issues. Furthermore, the resources—human, financial, and otherwise—that now go to supporting some of those older folks would now be freed up for other purposes. That can't help but lead to benefits all around!

TRANSPARENCY CHANGES EVERYTHING !!

lon·gev·i·ty

/lônˈjevədē/

a long duration of individual life.

> SINCE THE BEGINNING OF HUMAN EXISTENCE, **MANKIND HAS TRIED TO EXTEND OUR LIFESPANS.**

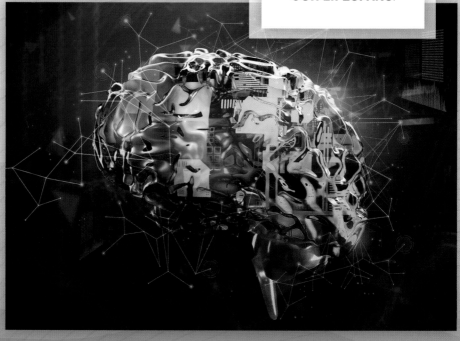

WHY **IT MATTERS:**

- Incorporating new habits may increase your life expectancy by ten, twenty, or thirty years!

ADVICE:

- Family first—taking care of your aging parents will not only prolong their lives, but yours as well.

- Genomics will play a significant role in health care going forward.

TAKE**AWAYS:**

- The 80% Rule—stop eating when you're 80% full.

- Eat a plant-based diet.

- Have a sense of purpose.

ACTION STEPS**:**

- Add one new longevity habit per quarter.

- Maintain your physical and financial well-being.

PART THREE
EXPONENTIAL
TRANSPARENCY

"A lack of transparency results in distrust and a deep sense of insecurity."

Dalai Lama

CHAPTER 16

Using the 6Ts

As you begin your quest to overcome obstacles, break through ceilings of complexity and improve relationships, slow things down, break apart the various elements and issues in your decision, and thereby reach clarity. The 6Ts of Exponential Transparency were created to help every person and company accomplish these outcomes. The 6Ts enable complex variables and issues to be simplified into a process providing optimal results.

As a reminder, the **6Ts of Exponential Transparency** comprise the following elements:

1 **TRANSPARENCY STANDARDS** 4 TRANSPARENT COST

2 **TERMS** 5 TRUTH

3 TOTAL ACCOUNTABILITY 6 **TRUST**

It's important to remember that each "T" is not equally important in every equation. Sometimes **terms** are the key to unlocking the answer, and other times you'll need to lean more heavily on **trust** and **transparent cost**. Nevertheless, by checking off each box and assigning it the appropriate level of weight and influence, you can eliminate the "noise" that often complicates solving important matters.

Apply the 6Ts to simple situations daily and soon you'll be able to utilize it to untwist even the seemingly most difficult knots.

Believing wholeheartedly in this process and applying it consistently in my personal and business life, part of my motivation and mission has been to spread the word. On a smaller scale, the 6Ts have been successfully used by many members of my team to overcome obstacles that are gumming up their progress. We start off the process by taking a step back and trying to identify the leading obstacle in their path. After that, we engage in a relatively informal dialogue, and the 6Ts magically assert themselves, typically leading to a resolution. Not only do they operate as a series of checks and balances upon our worst impulses, but they complement each other in a manner that makes their interaction result in progress that's more than the sum of its parts.

What's remarkable about the 6Ts is that you don't need to be a PhD or a quant or a Nobel Prize winner to use them. Not only are they easy to remember, but if you're truly honest with yourself and buy into the process, they're also remarkably easy to apply. In a world of gray, they often lead to black-and-white answers.

While there remain plenty of bad actors, I prefer to focus on the positives. The following is a summary of some "best practices" that I've either implemented or viewed others implement. You've likely been impacted positively by most or all of them.

LEARN TO APPLY THE 6Ts TO SIMPLE SITUATIONS ON A DAILY BASIS AND SOON YOU'LL BE ABLE TO UTILIZE IT AS A MEANS TO **UNTWIST EVEN THE SEEMINGLY MOST DIFFICULT KNOTS.**

A large part of the evolution of the 6Ts resulted from my long-term daily immersion in the financial industry. There are so many conflicts, so many failures to disclose, and so many sleight-of-hand tricks to keep the average consumer in the dark that the deck is consistently stacked against anyone not on the inside.

We have a regulatory system in place that tries to address many of these problems, but the fact is that with limited resources and manpower, and headwinds against it from lobbying efforts, it's tough to regulate all the nuances. It seems that someone is always able to find a loophole or obfuscate the true impacts of their actions.

1 TRANSPARENCY STANDARDS
EASY TO UNDERSTAND RULES LEADING TO HIGH LEVELS OF TRANSPARENCY.

My response to this asymmetry of information was to create what we consider an ideal **Transparency Standard**. PagnatoKarp led the way with the creation of True Fiduciary® Standards, ten simple and easy-to-understand "rules" that led directly to one of the highest levels of transparency in the industry and removal of many conflicts.

With respect to such standards, Apple is a shining star in the corporate world that all others should aspire to emulate. The world of technology is another playing field in which asymmetrical power and information often lead to bad practices. Companies can, in many cases, access, store, utilize, and sell clients' personal information without transparency or consent.

COMPANIES CAN IN MANY CASES ACCESS, STORE, UTILIZE AND SELL CLIENTS' PERSONAL INFORMATION **WITHOUT TRANSPARENCY OR CONSENT.**

Administ a or

PASSWORD:

1. Embrace the Legal Fiduciary Obligation to Place Clients' Interests First	2. Deliver Comprehensive Financial Planning	3. Provide Fee-Only Advice	4. Do Not Accept Commissions
Transparency Standards **True Fiduciary®** In Your Best Interest. **⊏PagnatoKarp**			5. Receive Only One Source of Revenue: Client Fees 6. Provide Transparency on Portfolios and Investments
10. Do Not Hold Any Client Assets, Securities or Money	9. Do Not Create Products to Sell or Price Any Public Securities	8. Measure Client Performance Returns Using Independent Third Parties	7. Remain Independent from any Bank, Broker Dealer, Insurance or Custodian

PagnatoKarp led the way with the creation of True Fiduciary® Standards, ten simple and easy-to-understand "rules" that led directly to one of the highest levels of transparency in the industry and removal of many conflicts.

In response to increasing concerns and to stay ahead of the curve, Apple created a privacy policy, a set of transparency standards for the access, storage, and utilization of client data. Every Apple product is designed from the ground up to protect personal information. Only the user can access the device. Your personal data belongs to you, Apple Pay transactions are private, and your data stays private. They also took the advanced step of providing a transparency report, which reveals information on government requests received.

TERMS

2

As for **Terms** of engagement, which function as the contract with the consumer, it is increasingly important that they be ridiculously simple and easy for anyone to understand. Lengthy disclaimers, small print, unclear pricing models, and legalese may provide a full picture if you have hours to analyze information and the skill set to do it, but those cases are the exception rather than the rule. In this context, simplicity is king.

Almost all of us have taken a taxi at some point or another. It's a necessity in urban and suburban life, and the transaction should be painless and friction-free. Unfortunately, over time the industry complicated pricing policies. Additionally, certain elements of the longstanding model created consumer uncertainty. For example, upon hailing a cab or calling for one, you typically do not know the exact cost of the cab ride, who the driver is, or what type of car will be picking you up. The pricing can vary wildly based on the length of time of the ride, the distance traveled, the time of day, and whether it's a weekday, weekend, or holiday. Different cab companies charge different rates. Different cities charge different rates.

Some cabs take Visa or MasterCard and some only take cash. The cabs that do take a credit card don't always maintain the infrastructure to do so—you arrive at your location without cash, and suddenly the process is at a standstill because the card processor is out of order. Of course, cab drivers always prefer the customer paying in cash, so you're left wondering if the "malfunctioning" machine is a ruse. On a more basic level, you have no idea who is picking you up or if the car is a compact two-door, four-door sedan, or an SUV. If you're a family of four headed off on a ski vacation and a two-door subcompact shows up, there's no way you'll get all your gear inside. Now you'll have to wait for another cab, which may prevent you from getting to your flight on time.

Uber saw this market inefficiency and built a business that is premised upon ridiculously simple terms. With a few simple clicks, the customer knows the exact cost of the ride and can make a seamless payment with no cash needed! Not only do you know your driver's name, but you have access to a great deal more information about them, including how many trips they have made and what prior riders' experiences have been. The customer knows the license plate number, make, model, and color of the car picking them up.

TOTAL ACCOUNTABILITY
HIGH QUALITY GOVERNANCE. DEFINABLE CONSEQUENCES. ADHERENCE TO STANDARDS AND TERMS.

Quality governance and operations are only possible and likely when operating within an ecosystem demanding **Total Accountability**. Companies and employees need to be held individually and collectively accountable for adhering to the transparency standards and terms that have been created. If there is complete clarity about the consequences of a failure to adhere to the standards and terms, then there's never any question about how, when, or why to act.

A prime example of this can be seen in everyday grocery shopping. For decades, there has been minimal accountability and transparency among growers, wholesalers, and retailers of food. For a long time, it was unclear when you bought a tomato, or an apple, or a piece of meat if it was genetically modified (GMO), if pesticides were used, or whether the working conditions of the farmers were humane. You had no way to discern whether sound and conscientious ecological practices were

followed. You transacted for that food, but its backstory and heritage were a black hole.

Once again, that vacuum was filled through responsible capitalism. Companies like Whole Foods have taken total accountability within the grocery food industry to a whole new level. They have created a 28-page supplier manual providing complete clarity on the terms, processes, and other criteria by which all vendors are held accountable. The manual is called "Responsibly Grown" and has a detailed rating system for every supplier and every product sold. In turn, the rating system provides transparency for consumers on soil health; air pollution impacts; energy impacts; climate impacts; waste-reduction practices; pest management; ecosystem details; biodiversity efforts; water conservation steps; and even the well-being of the farmers and the people working for the suppliers. Suppliers must adhere to a detailed ten-step process before being considered by Whole Foods. Every supplier must meet transparency and traceability standards, they must share detailed supply chain information, and they must commit to industry-driven traceability initiatives. Furthermore, all products must comply with clear standards for food safety, social accountability, and other factors related to food quality and environmental impacts.

> THE 6Ts APPROACH REQUIRES THAT ALL COSTS BE SUMMARIZED IN TOTAL AND **EASY FOR ANYONE TO UNDERSTAND.**

4 TRANSPARENT COST
COMPLETE AND TOTAL COST. NO HIDDEN FEES. SIMPLE TO UNDERSTAND.

The value of **transparent costs** should be self-evident, but as consumers we frequently accept the notion of hidden fees or charges that make an item cost substantially more than the expected price. Some businesses rely on these opaque costs to pad their bottom lines.

In contrast, a 6Ts approach would require that all costs be summarized in total and easy for anyone to understand.

Anyone who owns a home knows that the purchasing process can be nerve-wracking and fraught with uncertainty. That kind of stress makes what will likely be the largest single purchase consumers make in their lifetime even more stressful.

Unfortunately, as it has existed for decades, the reigning model makes understanding the real costs of purchasing your home exceptionally challenging. You may see a big round number listed on the initial advertisement or the eventual offer sheet, but when it comes time to cut the check, suddenly it increases substantially.

Where do all those add-ons and "necessary" fees come from?

The cost maze of buying a home starts with the real estate agent. Most people need a real estate agent to help find the home with the features they desire. Furthermore, the existing system provides a form of friction to doing it yourself—sometimes a real estate agent is the only means by which a prospective buyer can see inside a particular home.

Real estate agents may be very helpful, but they aren't doing this out of the goodness of their hearts. They are paid a commission upon the sale of a home, which means the only way they receive compensation is if a home is sold. Different real estate agents charge different rates of commission. When you sell, they take that rate off the top. If you're the buyer, it doesn't cost you directly, but those commissions are likely built into the cost of the home so, in effect, you are paying too.

HOME $500,000
+ $15K CLOSING COSTS + REALTOR 6%
ACTUAL COST:
$550,000

Of course, it's rare that a home is sold for the listing price. You might want to hold out for a price that's $10,000 more in either direction. Your realtor may consider "one in the hand" to be more valuable than a sale that might get delayed or canceled, so they push you to take the amount on the table, perhaps to your detriment. Who are they working for at that point?

Next, the buyer has to figure out the costs for various forms of insurance. Most times these insurances are required to borrow money to pay for the home, so the consumer really doesn't have a choice, but they are never factored into the home listing price. Examples of insurance include title insurance and Private Mortgage Insurance (PMI). The consumer then has to determine the costs to obtain a loan to pay for the property. Most loans have something called points. The mortgage industry uses the terminology of points versus commissions, further confusing the consumer. The points (costs) paid to obtain a loan are also not factored into a home's listing price.

Remember that home you planned to pay x amount of dollars for? Suddenly x has grown substantially. Increasingly, educated consumers are demanding greater transparency about what x really means.

TRUTH

5

OPEN, ACCURATE, DATA-BASED COMMUNICATION OF FACTS.

Implementation of all of these depends heavily on **truth**, the ability to openly and accurately communicate the facts. Any entity that fails to do so risks alienating both clients and employees.

So, what are the signs of a truth-based organization?

It's one that tends to be data-based, open, and factual with communication. Organizations like Starbucks and Glitch openly share their employees' compensation. Google's employees openly share their salaries on a posted intranet spreadsheet. It's not necessarily an easy transition to make, but it's the right one in most cases.

Prior to Netflix launching streaming videos, consumers did not know what movies would be available, what the rental costs would be, or when they would need to return the movie before incurring late fees at their local Blockbuster video store. Netflix now has 140 million users streaming their videos with complete truth on the availability and cost of any movie. Blockbuster? For that and other reasons, they're effectively gone.

6 TRUST
COMPLETE CONSUMER LOYALTY. EXPONENTIAL TRANSPARENCY.

Simply following the five preceding Ts is a direct roadmap to complete consumer loyalty and trust. Exponential transparency and trust go hand in hand. Think of each "T" as a building block, one placed on top of another. Each step in the transparency process is essential, each step builds upon those prior to it. As a result, each step leads inexorably to trust. If a company is experiencing a lack of employee or customer trust, one or more of the exponential transparency steps is missing. Reverse engineer where you have a gap and you can shore up the process, which in turn will lead to success.

As previously mentioned, The Vanguard Group is a beautiful example of flawless execution of the first five steps. Jack Bogle founded the company in 1974 and created the world's first index mutual fund in 1975. He relentlessly pursued exponential transparency for investors and the financial services industry more broadly, creating a set of transparency standards to help explain to individual investors their huge advantage over active management. Today, index funds make up most exchange-traded funds (ETFs) and provide complete transparency on every investment. Investors can buy and sell ETFs online at most major banks and broker-dealers without paying a commission. Shareholders always know exactly what they own.

Bogle created terms that were ridiculously easy for an investor to follow. He demanded total accountability across the board from every employee at Vanguard. The company and all employees have oversight and are heavily regulated by the Securities and Exchange Commission (SEC) and would be subject to penalties for violating SEC regulations, but Bogle insisted that they hold themselves to a higher standard.

Transparent cost prevails with every ETF created at Vanguard. The investors know exactly what the costs are before, during, and after making an investment. These costs can be found with a few simple clicks online or by speaking with a Vanguard representative. The costs are also transparently disclosed and easy to find in their brochures and literature. Jack Bogle instilled a culture of openly and accurately communicating the facts about every investment created at Vanguard, and the result was a culture of unvarnished truth. Whether you are an employee working at Vanguard or an investor, you always feel that there's a clear set of unbiased facts in front of you.

After decades of following the five core building blocks of exponential transparency, the company's brand is synonymous with trust.

After the horrors of the last recession, the general public's trust in the financial services industry remains tenuous. In direct contrast to that reality, Vanguard has experienced exponential growth in the same intervening time period amassing more than $5.3 trillion assets under management.

CLEARLY, FOLLOWING THE FIRST 5Ts TO ATTAIN THE 6th IS A **RECIPE FOR SUCCESS.**

I've chosen easily understandable examples in this chapter to help you understand how this process relates to every aspect of your life—from the most basic to the most complicated. When you find yourself at a crossroads, unsure of what to do, this is the road map to reaching the right conclusion.

1 TRANSPARENCY STANDARDS

- What is the #1 transparency issue in your industry or company?
- What conflicts exist that can be removed by a transparency standard?
- What items are opaque, vague, or not clear to your clients?
- What is the entity or universe that demands a set of standards?
- How many standards are optimal?
- How can the standards be crafted in a manner that is easy to understand?

2 TERMS

- Is the client contract ridiculously simple to understand?
- How many pages is the client agreement form?
- What medium is the contract—digital or hard copy?
- Is the client agreement form protecting the client or the company?
- How are complex terms explained simply?
- How can you "front load" the terms so that all parties are aware of them in advance?
- Is full disclosure being provided and easy to understand?

3 TOTAL ACCOUNTABILITY

- What are the employee and company repercussions for not adhering to the standards?
- Are the repercussions individual or collective?
- What third-party regulator is holding the company accountable?
- What company officer is holding employees accountable?
- How can parties entering into a transaction be fully aware that they are dealing on a level playing field?

4 TRANSPARENT COST

- Are costs ridiculously simple to understand?
- Are total client costs given in one number?
- Are all costs disclosed up front?
- Is a total provided that incorporates all costs?
- How can middlemen be eliminated?

5 TRUTH

- Is transparent data provided to clients?
- How can decisions be reduced to data?
- Is the client value proposition quantified?
- How can data be shared without alienating parties?
- What are the best methods for conveying information in an unbiased fashion?

6 TRUST

- How do the first five Ts interact to build a culture of trust?
- Which of the first five Ts are most critical to a given decision?
- How do you work to build a culture of trust every day?
- Do employees trust the company?
- Does the company share data and best practices with peers and competitors?
- Does your decision-making process seamlessly incorporate the 6Ts?

The world is getting more complicated and failure to change with the times will leave you behind, but by applying the 6Ts, you can stay ahead of the curve and ride the exponential "bend of the hockey stick"—the Transparency Wave—to levels you would not have thought possible before.

TRANSPARENCY CHANGES EVERYTHING !!

CHAPTER 16 | USING THE 6Ts

trust
/trəst/

firm belief in the reliability, truth, ability, or
strength of someone or something.

6Ts of Exponential
TRANSPARENCY

6 TRUST

5 TRUTH

4 TRANSPARENT COST

3 TOTAL ACCOUNTABILITY

2 TERMS

1 TRANSPARENCY STANDARDS

WHY **IT MATTERS:**

- Transparency will improve all aspects of one's life—social, business, health, and financial.

ADVICE:

- Utilize the 6Ts as building blocks of trust, each exponentially building on the next.
- Ask others to hold you accountable.
- Companies thriving today are data-based, open, and factual with communication.

TAKE**AWAYS:**

- Create transparency standards that are easy-to-understand rules leading to high levels of accountability.
- All humans have the ability to be transparent.
- Fear is the #1 obstacle to transparency.

ACTION STEPS:

- Block off time to create transparency standards to maximize your greatest opportunities.
- Utilize the 6Ts to develop your three pillars of longevity: 1. Financial Well-Being 2. Mobility 3. Social Engagement.
- Challenge your organization by asking transparency questions that facilitate deep thinking and dialogue.

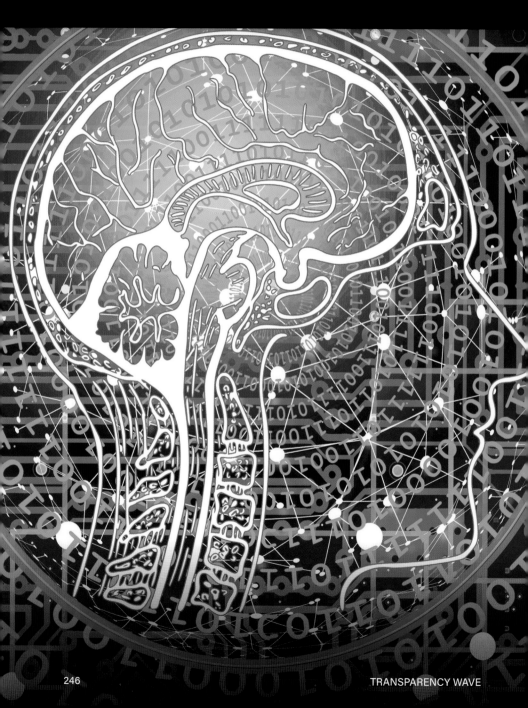

"BOTS HAVE ALREADY TAKEN OVER."

MANU SHARMA

CHAPTER 17

Artificial Intelligence

The term "artificial intelligence" (AI) doesn't have the world's best PR firm.

To many citizens, even educated ones who are likely to be early adopters of technology, it suggests a dystopian future in which we're all working for robots and have no interpersonal relationships.

Obviously, the term "intelligence" has a net-positive connotation, so it must be the word "artificial" that scares them. "Artificial" gets a bad rap. Sure, you may read that a food source has "no artificial ingredients," but just because something is "man-made" is not in and of itself an indicator of negative quality. That's what we need to get over—our preconceptions. AI experts, like **Dr. David Bray** and **Vint Cerf** from People-Centered Internet, would prefer the initials to stand for **Augmented Intelligence**. This may describe the essence of the technology in a more elegant and accurate way.

Rather than worrying about a world in which we work for robots, we need to build a world in which robots work to make our lives better. It is widely accepted that robots create many skilled jobs. We only need

ROBOTS CREATE JOBS AND MORE OF THE JOBS THAT RELATE TO THEM ARE SKILLED.

look at Germany as an example of a country with a high robot-to-citizen ration where unemployment is low.

If you think artificial intelligence can't achieve that, first you need to consider the ways that it has infiltrated our lives already.

For example, are you on a first-name basis with Alexa or Siri?

Whether you know it or not, AI is already a part of your life. While such technological advances were promised to us for decades, until recently they were mostly just that—promises, available in relatively primitive forms to the privileged few. In the last few years, however, the use of AI and its applications has exploded worldwide. It's not necessarily new. Many of us remember Deep Blue, the IBM computer that beat chess champion Garry Kasparov over 20 years ago, but its presence in your daily life is rapidly expanding. IBM's Watson went on the game show *Jeopardy* and won $77,000 on the first day and $1 million over three days.

What is AI? There's no single definition, but generally the term refers to the mimicry of human reasoning by machines. Today, we have

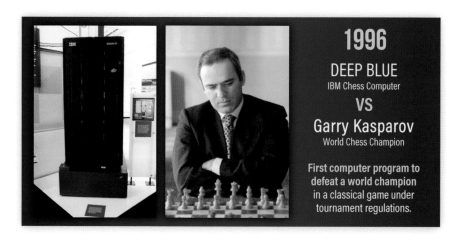

1996
DEEP BLUE
IBM Chess Computer
VS
Garry Kasparov
World Chess Champion

First computer program to defeat a world champion in a classical game under tournament regulations.

autonomous cars, speech-recognition programs, smart shopping, and strategic game systems, among other advances. As computing power and machine learning evolves over the next five to ten years, the advances in these arenas should be exponential.

How is this going to change the average American's life? It certainly appears that machines, in robot form or otherwise, are going to enhance and take the place of many workers. That applies not just to manual labor and service industry jobs, but also to highly skilled positions such as reading medical x-rays, conducting legal research, and performing surgery.

These advances are coming to the wealth management industry too. In fact, they're already here. That's where I was first exposed in-depth to their many applications and advantages. With the advent of "robo-advice," algorithm-driven platforms that can consider sophisticated and complicated questions objectively, wealth management is being democratized and available to a wider swath of the public, often at a lower cost than ever before. Ask a specific question and the program can quickly generate a data-driven answer at any time, mining information from around the globe.

As we expect to live longer, fuller lives, the need for quality advice becomes all that much more critical—in finance and other spheres of life. By removing the agendas and subjectivity—and replacing it with

IBM'S WATSON WINS $1,000,000 ON THE GAME SHOW JEOPARDY.

measured, dispassionate advice—you can, in many cases, get a more objective outcome. If designed and employed appropriately, it can remove unnecessary complexity from your life and allow you to focus on the things that make you happiest and most productive.

There is no telling where AI will lead, but the goal should be to use it to live longer, more vibrant lives.

One of the thought leaders I turn to on this topic is my friend Manu Sharma, an innovator, entrepreneur, and influential thinker in Silicon Valley, the founder and CEO of Labelbox, a company dedicated to accelerating access to artificial intelligence. If those credentials alone don't wow you, he's also an aerospace engineer (aka, rocket scientist) with a master's degree from Stanford. His engineering background led him to his current career.

"I was working in a company called 'Planet Labs,' which has the highest number of satellites by a magnitude more than any other company or even a government entity" Sharma said. "They're scanning the Earth every single day as Google Maps just updates with the latest images. So, the company is getting so much data from around the world that is useful for farmers to detect problems in their farms or for insurance companies, or the finance industry, or basically seeing Google trends. There's a big gap between those insights versus the data. And AI has, by far, the best shot at bridging that gap. So, a farmer in the Midwest may get an alert that identifies some nitrogen deficiency in a portion of the farm. Maybe their team needs to apply more nitrogen that day. And those kinds of insights are going to increase our productivity as a society overall and make more data-driven decisions."

Sharma continued to say, "I saw a potential for AI and how poor some of the practices were to build AI. I wanted to solve that, so that made me move to this industry. But what is fascinating is that, at the core, it's more about building software and building business on building software. It's very different than traditional industries where the companies are building hardware and just the long cycles of iterations. In software, we are putting in new improvements every single day."

Specifically, they are mimicking the neurons of the human brain via software and by creating "hundreds of millions of them; you can train them to make predictions of any kind."

Sharma said that a big part of the expansion of AI in recent years is the result of the intersection of Moore's Law and economic realities. A decade ago, it wasn't financially feasible for many businesses or industries to apply AI to their problem-solving needs. Now, however, the processing units needed to apply AI to a wide variety of problems have come down so far in price that it has become profitable to employ them. That's the power of exponential growth.

What industries will AI benefit most? It's hard to say through our subjective lenses and less-than-computer-like understanding of data, but any endeavor that depends on the sifting of massive amounts of data has great potential to benefit. He explained that the amount of data produced isn't the only factor in figuring out which ones will adapt most quickly.

"Health care has huge amounts of data, but accessing health-care data is extremely hard," Sharma explained. "Health care has the highest potential to transform our lives, but it is probably going to be slower to adapt AI in all segments. Plus, it's regulated, so there will need to be new standards and new laws created to kind of embrace AI in prescriptive and diagnostic areas. Manufacturing is probably an easier

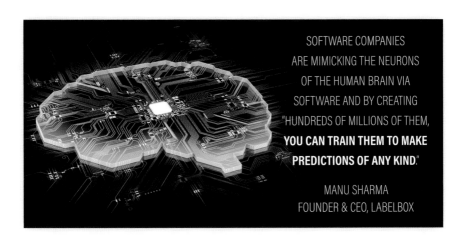

SOFTWARE COMPANIES ARE MIMICKING THE NEURONS OF THE HUMAN BRAIN VIA SOFTWARE AND BY CREATING "HUNDREDS OF MILLIONS OF THEM, **YOU CAN TRAIN THEM TO MAKE PREDICTIONS OF ANY KIND."**

MANU SHARMA
FOUNDER & CEO, LABELBOX

one. We are already seeing many companies making a big change in their industries. I think the industry that would be most impacted is generally like the Internet. You notice it in all the software that we use daily, whether it's email, phones, or different apps. On an average day, I would probably provide more data to my phone than anything else. And that data is sort of food for AI."

The benefits in those areas alone will contribute mightily to longevity and life satisfaction.

Nevertheless, I don't want to be a Pollyanna and assume that exponential progress can occur without at least a few hiccups, speedbumps, and hurdles along the way. Sharma, who like me, is a huge cheerleader for the possibilities of AI, addressed the differences between fear and caution directly.

"I think the fear about robots taking over the world is sort of legitimate but also kind of exaggerated because **robots have already taken over**," he explained. "I think it's a relative term and I think it will always be the case that we would be fearful of some massive changes in the industry. But what I think is really exciting is AI taking over the work that is highly repetitive, which is only going to create more opportunities for people to concentrate on more creative work, or perhaps even utilize AI to create more wealth spreading around the world. **Just like any other power, AI can be used to create great, valuable things in society**. It can also be used to make harmful things and that is an ultimate question that is posed to all of us: how do we use AI for better-use cases than the harmful ones?"

What are the areas to be concerned about?

Sharma thinks that a worst-case scenario would be a situation where, in fifty or a hundred years, potentially within our lifetimes, nations

---

JUST LIKE ANY OTHER POWER, **AI CAN BE USED TO CREATE GREAT, VALUABLE THINGS IN SOCIETY**.

could utilize extreme AI capabilities to create an extreme advantage in warfare. We have historical precedent, of course, for countries to use any advantage they can develop in that context, but the exponential growth in this arena makes it scarier, on par with the invention of nuclear weapons. "Historically, that's what nations have done," he said, but he chooses to apply a PMA filter instead, noting that there will be ways to "harness or capitalize on" those same technologies in a manner which results in "a net benefit for the world."

His concerns involve the **manipulation of data.**

"One big fear I do have is the kind of things we observed in the recent elections," Sharma explained. "What is really interesting is that humans have started spending more time online using social media and email. People are trying to capitalize on that human attention online and starting to promote opinions. It's quite a powerful thing now. You could polarize or influence a big demographic of people by pushing some content and a lot of these things are done by AI algorithms. One can argue that this trend is great because people can reach out and influence the agenda or spread the agenda more easily. You don't have to organize people. We don't have to come to one hall and listen to people, but it's also very scary what happens if someone comes with billions of dollars to promote one idea and suddenly that idea is captured by all peoples' minds. So, yes, this whole venue is quite scary."

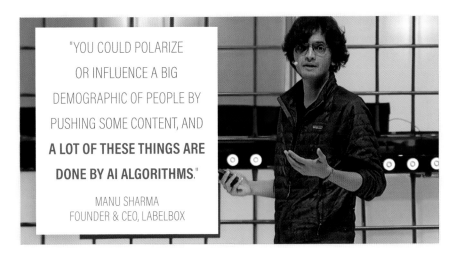

"YOU COULD POLARIZE OR INFLUENCE A BIG DEMOGRAPHIC OF PEOPLE BY PUSHING SOME CONTENT, AND **A LOT OF THESE THINGS ARE DONE BY AI ALGORITHMS.**"

MANU SHARMA
FOUNDER & CEO, LABELBOX

In Chapter 3, we discussed the Digital Wave and the 6Ds. The second D represents the deceptive period an industry goes through before acceptance. This is the bottom of the exponential curve, before an industry grows by 10x. This is exactly where we are with AI, and here are examples from my personal daily experiences.

Let's start with our home. As the CEO of a growing business and an empty nester, my wife and I travel extensively, and we are home only 25% of the time. While we are on the road, AI is running our home. The Nest system allows us to direct everything right from our cell phones. We can be traveling in Europe and adjust the room temperature, turn lights on and off, view any deliveries arriving, or anyone appearing at the front door at home. We can connect to smoke detectors and the security system, sound system, surveillance around the home, door locks, and much more. When traveling in our car, the Tesla autopilot does 80% of the driving.

My wife and I do 90% of our shopping online, including groceries. AI makes this ridiculously simple—the bots know what we like, where we buy from, and it only takes one click. Items are delivered the same or next day to our home, hotel, or vacation rental. My health is being monitored 24/7 with my Apple Watch. AI lets me know my heart rate, provides an instant electrocardiogram, and analyzes my sleep patterns. It tells me when to take a deep breath and calculates my calories

THE BOTS KNOW WHAT WE LIKE, WHERE WE BUY FROM, AND IT ONLY **TAKES ONE CLICK.**

burned, glucose level, and a ton of other items. AI books the morning yoga class, that evening's dinner reservation, and all my travel. When reaching the age of fifty, it's essential to undergo the uncomfortable medical requirement of a colonoscopy. Due to AI, I'm now able to have a virtual colonoscopy (approved by my doctor) that doesn't require being put under anesthesia. A year ago, my father had a life-threatening heart condition, and 95% of the surgery was performed by a robot. This year he is fully recovered and took the trip of a lifetime around the world.

In my wealth management business, every part of our firm uses AI daily. Our portfolio managers, financial planners, traders, CPA's, attorneys, lifestyle concierges, and family coaches all rely upon it. We would not be able to perform Intelligent Wealth Management™ and fuse our multi-family office services without the utilization of AI.

I'm in total agreement with Manu Sharma's quote: "Bots have already taken over," and it's beautiful!!

TRANSPARENCY CHANGES EVERYTHING !!

PERSPECTIVES

CHAPTER 17 | ARTIFICIAL INTELLIGENCE

ALL DAY, EVERY DAY!!

WHY **IT MATTERS:**

- Artificial Intelligence (AI) and bots have already taken over our daily lives as we encounter apps, emails, texts, surveillance security, Siri and Alexa, social media, music and video streaming, online banking, and credit cards.

- Utilizing AI for positive ends provides more of our most valuable asset: TIME!

ADVICE:

- Utilize artificial intelligence and bots to focus on your passions and spend more time with the people you love.

TAKE**AWAYS:**

- "Augmented Intelligence" describes the essence of AI technology in a more elegant and accurate way than the commonly used vernacular.

- A big part of AI expansion in recent years is the result of the intersection of Moore's Law and economic realities.

- AI is creating more opportunities for people to concentrate on more creative work.

ACTION STEPS:

- Experiment with new AI tools. Enable the tools to provide a renewed focus on what matters most to you.

- Consider tools that positively impact your health, financial well-being, and relationships, particularly those that free up more time for your passions and goals.

"A blockchain is just a database that is maintained by a network of users and secured through cryptography."

Daniel Oberhaus

CHAPTER 18

Cutting-Edge Technologies: Blockchain

What do the dominant, life-changing technologies of the future look like?

Well, to some degree, we can't predict what they'll be, how they'll be structured, or what they'll accomplish. Things are moving at such a rapid pace, by the time we fully integrate a concept into our minds, it could be outdated or squashed by a better iteration.

Remember MySpace? It got crushed by Facebook, which in turn got supplemented by Twitter, Snapchat, and Instagram, among others.

Betamax begat VHS, which led to DVDs, and now we have streaming video.

Those are evolutions of technology, and even when one model is supplanted by another, usually there's a semi-direct path from one to another; they are trying to reach the same basic goal. Hopefully that goal is to make our lives easier, better, more profitable, and longer, in some combination.

Not all technological advances, even those that are clearly superior, win the footrace forward. Remember Google Glass? They were "smart glasses" that crammed many of the features of a smartphone into a hands-free intuitive device. Now your eyeglasses (a revolutionary thirteenth- or fourteenth-century breakthrough) were being substantially updated for the first time in hundreds of years. They had more computing power than the Space Shuttle and advocates could think of dozens if not hundreds of applications that would benefit a wide swath of society and industries.

Of course, as with any nascent technology, there were concerns. First and foremost, civil rights advocates worried about the privacy impacts on both wearers and people within the wearers' sightlines. Others claimed that there were negative safety ramifications, e.g., distractions caused by driving while wearing them.

Ultimately, Google weighed the good and the bad, the policy concerns, and the marketplace realities, and decided to delay the continuation of the program for several years.

Does that mean Google Glass was a failure?

Hardly. They may never gain ubiquity, but some form of smart glasses may ultimately become as widely used as our smartphones. For a technology to succeed, the proper framework must be in place. Disruption is often key, but without the proper backdrop, it will fail. Think of it this way: What if Mark Zuckerberg's father had invented

Facebook in the early 1970's? It might have had the same appeal and social value, but without widespread use of home computers (and subsequently smartphones), it wouldn't have had the path to gain any traction and would have died an early death. For a technology to succeed, not only does the public have to be ready to accept it, but you must have the technological, regulatory, and financial ability to integrate it into individual lives. There's a cost-benefit analysis involved, too. We might develop a pill that cures or significantly slows cancer, but if it costs $5 million a pop, few people will be able to justify its cost, no matter how badly they're suffering—and without a critical mass to make it commercially feasible, no one may deem it worthwhile to produce it.

That's why I'm so excited about this point in history. The rapid growth of technology, combined with a "tipping point" in terms of peoples' willingness to accept or try it, has merged with our legal, regulatory, and economic abilities and goals.

What does that mean in plain language?

It means that there is less "friction" in the ability for advances to move forward. And the technology that is often cited as reducing friction the most is blockchain.

WHAT IS BLOCKCHAIN?

The clearest explanation I've seen came from author Daniel Oberhaus: "At its core, a blockchain is just a database that is maintained by a network of users and secured through cryptography. When new information is added to the database, it is parceled in 'blocks,' which can be thought of as containers for this data. Every so often, a new block is created and linked to a 'chain' of previously created blocks. Each block has a unique ID called a hash that is created by running the ID of the block that preceded it and the data stored in the current block through a cryptographic algorithm. This ensures the integrity of all the data stored on the blockchain because altering the data in any block would produce a different hash."[1]

What does that mean?

In conventional shorthand, it signifies that there is an ongoing ledger of each transaction that occurs in a particular space, with an inalterable electronic timestamp showing when a particular good changed hand. It has been around since the early 1990's, but over the past few years it has gained not only widespread awareness, but also the technological backbone to make it functional.

The most notable or widely known use of blockchain technology is in cryptocurrencies like Bitcoin and Ethereum. Among those not steeped in the vernacular, "blockchain" and "cryptocurrency" are often used interchangeably. That's a mistake. Cryptocurrency is a use of blockchain, but they are not synonymous.

The best explanation I've seen of how to differentiate the two came from CIO Saeed Elnaj in *Forbes*: "In a simple metaphoric comparison, blockchain is like an engine that can be used in airplanes, vehicles, elevators, escalators, washers, and dryers. Bitcoin, meanwhile, is like the first Ford Model T **car that was manufactured in 1908. This fundamental difference helps in understanding the polymorphic value of blockchain and the problems with** Bitcoin and most cryptocurrencies."

Cryptocurrencies are one area where blockchain will have value, but they're not the only such venue. It could be used to ensure the integrity of elections or to make sure that humanitarian donations of rations reach their intended recipients. Any time there's reason to believe that a government or dominant institution can't be trusted, or that there's too much "friction" in a set of transactions, it'll act as a safeguard. As essayist and risk analyst Nassim Nicholas Taleb said, it's "an insurance policy against an Orwellian future."[2]

Because new technologies are threatening to both institutions and to expectations, they often inspire devoted cadres of supporters and detractors. It can be hard to discern the truth because the former group overlooks anything negative about the technology, while the latter group sees everything about it as predictive of its ultimate failure or misuse. For example, Tesla's performance on Wall Street is often determined by two groups: Those who think of Elon Musk as a visionary genius who can do no wrong, and those who think he's a snake oil salesman with an intent to deceive. The truth, if there is one, in most cases lies in neither of those extremes but in between. Its position on the continuum may be closer to one than the other, but we do ourselves a disservice if we don't acknowledge both the pros and cons.

One of the cons right now is volatility. To use Bitcoin as an example, when I first came up with the idea for this book, one Bitcoin was trading at about $18,000. As I write these pages, it's somewhere under $9,000 per bitcoin and fluctuating fairly substantially on a day-to-day basis. At that rate, it would be foolishness to either accept it or pay it for your daily Starbucks coffee. You might be getting a latte for a nickel, or it might be costing you fifty bucks.

Other criticisms include the amount of energy it takes to mine a Bitcoin, the possibility of tampering or rigging cryptocurrency markets, and the fact that unlike fiat currencies, it is not backed by the full faith and credit of any government (which can be viewed as a feature rather than a bug if you phrase it properly).

Some critics have compared it to historical bubbles, including the Dutch "Tulip Mania" of the 17th century.[3] Famed investor Warren Buffett told CNBC that Bitcoin is "probably rat poison squared."[4] His colleague

Charlie Munger had similar feelings and made fun of the rush to buy Bitcoin, claiming that "it's just dementia. It's like somebody else is trading turds and you decide you can't be left out."[5]

> PEOPLE WHO ARE COMFORTABLE WITH THE STATUS QUO DON'T RESPOND WELL TO CHANGE, **EVEN IF THEY ARE HIGHLY INTELLIGENT.**

Those kinds of hyperbolic statements may make for great headlines, but they don't help the average consumer. A measured approach would have been to explain what they think is wrong with Bitcoin, and then help educate, rather than go for the five second soundbite. No matter how accomplished both Buffett and Munger might be, those soundbites are not for caution but rather an expression of *fear* (remember the bear?). People who are comfortable with the status quo don't respond well to change, even if they are highly intelligent. My goal is to only be afraid when I should be afraid, and information is the best means to avoid being afraid at the wrong times.

I would not be a responsible financial advisor, let alone a True Fiduciary®, taking the word of one side over the other. It doesn't matter if it's Ray Kurzweil or Warren Buffett or Bill Gates—a big part of my job is sorting out the wheat from the chaff. After spending hundreds of hours reading about blockchain and its associated products, and talking to dozens of experts, I've worked hard to understand both the technology and its applications, and here's where I stand:

BLOCKCHAIN WILL BE TRANSFORMATIVE.

Note, I did not say that Bitcoin or Ethereum will be transformative. I did not say with any level of certainty that it will change elections or charitable giving or any other segment of society. Indeed, one of the beauties of many technologies is that we don't necessarily know their ideal uses at the time of conception, but rather only after they mature. Think of them as infants: you may believe that your baby will become an all-pro running back, but you won't be disappointed if he becomes a nuclear physicist instead. Or you might want him to be a world-class violinist, but his talents down the road might be better suited to sculpting.

Just because a particular technology does not live up to its hype in one arena doesn't mean that it has completely failed. Remember the Internet bubble from the end of the last century? Companies like Pets.com were the face of the "Internet revolution," and they spent huge sums of money to advertise and gain market share before ultimately going belly-up. Their failure, however, does not signify the failure of the Internet as a whole. When they ceased to exist, no one with any foresight at all suggested that "we need to give up on this whole Internet experiment." In fact, I'd bet that most people today, in the United States and around the world, integrate the Internet into their lives more comprehensively than they ever could have expected in the year 2000.

In other words, sometimes even exponential technologies require steps and growing pains before they hit their true stride.

WHAT ARE SOME EXAMPLES OF BLOCKCHAIN'S POTENTIAL?

One of the oft-cited examples that excites me is the ability to provide financial stability and resources to underserved people around the world. Right now, there are an estimated two billion people around the world who do not have access to bank accounts. Think of what that

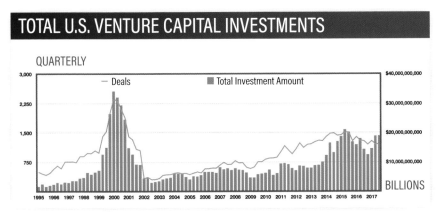

Quarterly U.S. venture capital investments, 1995–2017

RIGHT NOW, THERE ARE AN ESTIMATED **2 BILLION PEOPLE** AROUND THE WORLD WHO DO NOT HAVE ACCESS TO BANK ACCOUNTS.

means: they can't protect their assets, they can't build upon them, and it's difficult to save. The unbanked percentage of the world's population is appreciably different than it was a decade ago, but there's been one major change—they have access to the Internet (even in ultra-remote regions) and a surprisingly large percentage of them have smartphones.

This hits home for me when thinking back on the fishing trip to the Amazon basin in Brazil. Contrary to our group's belief, virtually everyone in the village we visited was connected with a smartphone. Five to 10 years ago they might not have had a clue about American music, geography or world events, but now they are as connected as anyone in a major city worldwide. If they weren't banked before, that opportunity now exists and that changes everything for them as individuals and as a culture. It brings opportunities for prosperity, happiness, and longevity that were previously denied as a result of where they were born.

In a nutshell, that's breaking down barriers through a reduction in friction!

Imagine you lived in Zimbabwe, an African nation that has gone through a period of hyperinflation, most notably from 2008 through 2009. During that time frame, the rate of inflation was estimated to be 79.6 billion%.[6] They started to issue currency in the billions and trillions

of Zimbabwe dollars, to the point that they became worthless. Eventually only foreign currency was accepted because the native bills were literally not worth the paper they were printed on.

What were the negative effects of Zimbabwe's hyperinflation?

Well, there was political unrest. A black market for goods arose, undermining the legitimate marketplace, and leading generations of citizens to inescapable poverty. The government never took any meaningful steps to stabilize their monetary system until they ultimately accepted other countries' currencies as both legal tender and their reserve currency, but by then the damage to the society had been done and the great evidence of President Mugabe's violations of human rights made recovery impossible.

But what if those suffering Zimbabwean citizens had access to non-state, frictionless banking institutions and currencies? Might the level of volatility that makes cryptocurrency currently unattractive as legal tender to many Americans be acceptable to people in less-stable economies? Does the "right" application of a technological instrument depend on your circumstances? I think it does. Blockchain might have

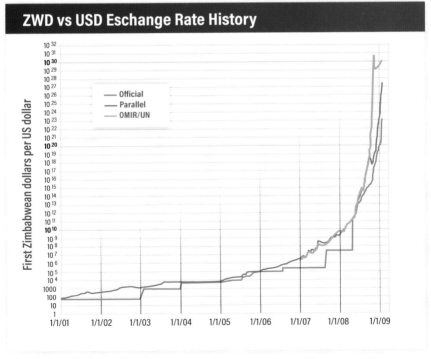

Official, black market, and OMIR exchange rates 1 Jan 2001 to 2 Feb 2009. SOURCE: wikipedia.org

very different applications for someone in my shoes than it does for an impoverished sub-Saharan African farmer.

It's not just people in remote villages who will benefit. Do you know the fastest way to get $10,000 from my home near Washington, DC, to someone in London, England, in 2019? You have to put it in a suitcase, get on a plane, and hand deliver it. That's crazy in the 21st century, but it's true. If you needed to follow that path, not only would it result in a loss of time and a risk of somehow losing the money, but even at a discount fare, that's a hell of tax/commission/penalty to pay for making a simple transaction.

Once my mind combined the increasing ubiquity of smartphones and the existing impediments to smooth and uncorrupted transactions, I saw the value of blockchain—if not its ultimate end game.

At that point, I turned to one of the experts I consult with most frequently for questions about blockchain generally, cryptocurrencies specifically, or really any matters about the intersection of technology, law, and business: Nathana Sharma from Singularity University. Nathana earned JD and MBA degrees from Yale Law School and the Yale School of Management, and while she still practices law, she does so much more than that. One of her greatest passions and greatest areas of expertise is the application of blockchain technology and artificial intelligence.

She rejects the typical arguments against blockchain. She doesn't dismiss their possibility but believes that at most they will be just speed bumps. When a technology has the possibility of becoming transformative, with an army of true believers behind it, concerns about energy use, volatility, and other factors are not absolute roadblocks.

In fact, she even rejects calling many of them "cryptocurrencies," instead preferring the term "digital assets," and she's helped me to see those distinctions. That's part of the problem with these emerging technologies: there are so many buzzwords and fads and levels of misinformation that it takes an expert like Nathana to guide you through them.

"When you've got something very new and you've got people thinking there's a lot of money to be made and you've got a lot of hype, you unfortunately have some people who will take advantage of others," Nathana said. "I think a lot of the projects that are currently out there in blockchain technology are just not high-quality projects. They won't stand the test of time. That was the case in the days of the early Internet too, and even before the Internet. I do think that it's important to be really counseled about how one gets exposure to the space if one chooses to do that because I think many of the projects that are currently valued in the top fifty won't be around in a year."

There will be swindlers and charlatans in the mix, but the antidote to that is to become educated. You don't throw out the baby with the bathwater. It's like medicine. There have been pharmaceuticals that have been dangerous and have had long-term negative effects, but only a minuscule percentage of society says that we should do away with medicine altogether. The good far outweighs the bad. The 0.1% that is bad gets the headlines, but the positive impacts from the 99.9% do so much "good" that it would be ridiculous to make some sort of blanket prohibition. Again, information is the antidote to fear. I'm not telling you to avoid precautions when you take a new medication or go in for surgery. Some level of concern or anxiety is normal. At the same time, a large part of life is about maximizing percentages, and the benefits of a given procedure almost always substantially outweigh its risks. If they didn't, you wouldn't go down that path.

HOW DO WE GET THE WIDEST GROUP OF POSSIBLE PARTICIPANTS TO UTILIZE AND BENEFIT FROM BLOCKCHAIN?
IT STARTS WITH TRANSPARENCY.

"What's cool about the crypto space is that it's right at the heart of what transparency gets you," Nathana said. "So, if you kind of step back and think about it, one of the things you have with crypto and blockchain is you start to have decentralized sharing of information. Think about how spending normally works. You have a centralized authority, whether it's Visa or MasterCard. You have some person who says, 'Okay, well, this identity of this seller is matching up with that identity of that one,' and they move the money around. And there's a central repository that's controlling that. When you start to decentralize, you can get a bunch of benefits if you open peer-to-peer interactions in a new way. People cannot understand how much cash they have or how they can move it around, and this is the first time that we can have the digital equivalent of cash. And there's a lot of different things that we can do with that. It is kind of like different flavors. One flavor is more anonymous than cash or kind of the anonymous equivalent of cash. But we can also have something like the current Bitcoin Network, where you know exactly the balance and the addresses of the whole network. It's just totally transparent who's doing what. We can argue about how much we want that, but it starts to become possible with blockchain technology."

That transparency is not additive—it's exponential!

"This technology can be used to increase transparency in a range of other areas," Nathana added. "So, it comes to supply chain management. That's a really important place for people in blockchain technology because we can start to have a few highly centralized secure tracking mechanisms of supply chains. You can start having more transparency into where your food is coming from."

She also suggested that pharmaceutical tracking would be a prime use for the blockchain in the future. Not only can you ensure that the right person in the right place is getting the right pill at the right time, but you can head off abuses. I immediately thought of the opioid crisis and how we could hamstring it if we could have a constant ledger of medicines' locations and provenances.

It's going to unlock business potential in ways we never thought possible. Sharma summed it up using Airbnb as a template.

"In the 1980s, if you said, '30 years from now, one of the biggest companies in the world is going to be kind of like a hotel but won't own any real estate and people are going to be renting rooms in each other's homes,' people would have thought you were crazy. You know, it was not possible to start to unlock that level of value until people had other pieces of the Internet. And then, over time, people started to use this new technology. They started coming up with new applications, and whether it's cloud computing—people thought cloud computing was crazy when it was first developed, and it took a whole lot of work to get into a place where it could be used—they could be used for a wide range of activities. I think we're going to see decentralized applications that are very hard for us to imagine today. This is one that's going to unlock an exponential level of value."

"WHAT'S COOL ABOUT THE CRYPTO SPACE IS THAT IT'S **RIGHT AT THE HEART OF WHAT TRANSPARENCY GETS YOU**."

NATHANA SHARMA
GENERAL COUNSEL, LABELBOX

Again, I use Nathana as a guide to understand these technologies and call upon her frequently. Transparency depends on finding the right sources. It's about trust, but once you have that, you can immerse yourself in the fun parts, the big-picture benefits. As an aside, while writing about her influence, I realized that she was something of a unicorn: a woman at the top levels of tech and business. While there are more than there were 20, 10, or five years ago, they're still in the minority. The impediments (i.e., friction) to their participation is dissipating, and it's women like Nathana who are making that happen. Not only are they breaking barriers and refusing to take "no" for an answer, but they're also encouraging other women to get involved in these spaces through conferences and mentoring.

I'm proud to say that I have a healthy balance of trusted sources and mentors from all demographics and a wide variety of walks of life. Thinking about this book, three of the experts I've quoted most extensively are Dr. Laura Carstensen, Dr. Lisa Genova, and Nathana Sharma.

"The financial world has, for the most part, not been inclusive to a number of groups, including women," Sharma said. "Women weren't even able to have their own credit cards in the 1970s. We are living in a world where engagement in finance generally is just more challenging for women and other groups that have been discriminated against. You know, certain racial groups have been unfairly targeted. It makes folks scared. You know, 'once bitten, twice shy.' I mean, there's a very small number of people in the world right now who control most of its wealth. And if those people decide this technology is really better for managing the world's money, I think we could see it happen regardless of widespread participation. That said, I want to see widespread participation. I think we have an incredible opportunity for the development of new kinds of wealth, and I want to see that happen. And I think part of how that will ultimately happen is by education."

PMA tells me that all the excitement and debate about blockchain is not only good for promoting the technology itself, but also for allowing various viewpoints to be heard.

TRANSPARENCY CHANGES EVERYTHING !!

> "...THERE'S A VERY SMALL NUMBER OF PEOPLE IN THE WORLD RIGHT NOW WHO CONTROL MOST OF ITS WEALTH. AND IF THOSE PEOPLE DECIDE THIS TECHNOLOGY IS REALLY BETTER FOR MANAGING THE WORLD'S MONEY, **I THINK WE COULD SEE IT HAPPEN...**"
>
> NATHANA SHARMA, GENERAL COUNSEL, LABELBOX

CHAPTER 18 | CUTTING EDGE TECHNOLOGIES: BLOCKCHAIN

block·chain

/ˈbläkˈCHān/

a system in which a record of transactions made in bitcoin or another cryptocurrency are maintained across several computers that are linked in a peer-to-peer network.

WHY **IT MATTERS:**

- Blockchain is a dominant, life-changing technology that has already arrived.

- Governments, including the United States, China, Japan, Singapore, the United Kingdom, Brazil, Switzerland, Georgia, and Uganda, all use blockchain for various purposes.

- Top companies, like Amazon, Microsoft, Google, Facebook, Apple, IBM, Accenture, JP Morgan, Bank of America, American Express, Tesla, Ford, Goldman Sachs, ExxonMobil, Walmart, Nestle, Pfizer, Anheuser-Busch, Samsung, and Berkshire Hathaway, all use blockchain technology.

ADVICE:

- Technology, blockchain, and transparency are all correlated and growing exponentially.

- The truth normally lies somewhere between extreme pessimism and extreme optimism.

- Anyone connected to the Internet can utilize a digital wallet.

TAKE**AWAYS:**

- Blockchain is a database that is maintained by a network of users and secured through cryptography.

- The most widely-known use of blockchain technology is Bitcoin. There have been over 450 billion Bitcoin transactions.

- Bitcoin can be used to purchase any product or service with a Visa card or digital wallet.

- The 1.7 billion unbanked adults worldwide may never need a bank thanks to blockchain and digital wallets.

ACTION STEPS**:**

- Allocate time to understand and utilize cutting-edge technologies like blockchain. These technologies are unleashing exponential transparency and results.

"ALWAYS SEEK THE
FLOURISHING OF OTHERS."

PAUL PAGNATO

CHAPTER 19

Advancing Your Purpose

Dan Buettner was quoted back in Chapter 15 on the characteristics and habits that exceptionally long-lived people often have in common. He mentioned that the Okinawans use of the word "Ikigai" and the Nicoyans a similar term, "plan de vida."

Both, he said, translate roughly into "why I wake up in the morning" and he explained that '**knowing your sense of purpose is worth up to seven extra years of life expectancy**."

What would you do for an extra seven years of a great life?

What are you doing to prepare for an extra seven years of a great life?

The two questions are closely related, and it involves knowing WHY you wake up in the morning. Your personal "greater purpose" doesn't have to be massively transformative, although you can certainly aim for that. It can involve a hobby, your family, a pursuit, or even just a general theme—but you need to have a **WHY**.

I've found mine in the concept of **True Fiduciary**®, an effort to embrace (and lead others in my primary industry to embrace) the legal fiduciary obligation to place clients' interests first. We aim to simplify complexity in the financial sector in a manner that will positively impact one million lives through True Fiduciary® transparency.

Transparency Standards | **True Fiduciary**®

1. Embrace the legal fiduciary obligation to place clients' interests first.
2. Deliver comprehensive financial planning.
3. Provide fee-only advice.
4. Do not accept commissions.
5. Receive only one source of revenue: client fees.
6. Provide transparency on portfolios and investments.
7. Remain independent from any bank, broker-dealer, insurance, or custodian.
8. Measure client performance returns using independent third parties.
9. Do not create products to sell or price any public securities.
10. Do not hold any client assets, securities, or money.

So then, how does someone who's a CEO of a nascent company, or someone in any other sphere of society, find their calling in a manner that will lead to a better and simpler life?

It's a pretty big lift, isn't it?

No. On the contrary, it's ridiculously simple and easy. The goal should be to put yourself in the shoes of the client, or the person on the other end.

It's all about seeking the flourishing of others: the proverbial "**doing well by doing good**."

When starting in this business, I could only have dreamed that I'd end up where I am today. I didn't come from money. I had no network, sales or marketing experience, or financial literacy. In fact, it took me one year and ten interviews with ten different wealth management offices to land a job.

The path from that point to now (and beyond) came by asking a simple question: "If I had $100,000, which I certainly did not have at the time, what would it take for me to give it to somebody to invest on my behalf?"

All I did was put myself in the shoes of some other reasonable man or woman.

What would they want? The answer came quickly: "Well, I'm going to need to trust that person."

Trust was a building block for the answer. **Transparency equals trust**. So, I'm going to need to earn trust. I'm going to need to be educated, and I'm going to need to have a game plan. None of that is metaphysical or complicated. It's relatively simple. It's like a 3-legged stool of preparedness: trust, information, and strategy.

Remember, I had never been in this business before, had no institutional knowledge or contacts to fall back on. There would be no "mulligans." My first mistake could very well be my last, because messing up someone's portfolio or plan, might mean never getting another shot to fix it.

The realization that asking and answering those simple questions was the basis for success provided the epiphany. Business is not the only forum in which "seeking the flourishing of others" can lead to benefits for all parties. The question itself is universally applicable. Ask it every time you're forced to make a tough or sticky decision, and it will always lead you in the right direction. It might not provide the specific details in every instance, but you'll be surprised at how often it gets you 50%, 75%, or even 90% of the way to where you want to end up.

WHAT'S **YOUR** WHY?

APPLY THE 6TS OF EXPONENTIAL TRANSPARENCY
TO LEAD DIRECTLY TO YOUR "WHY":

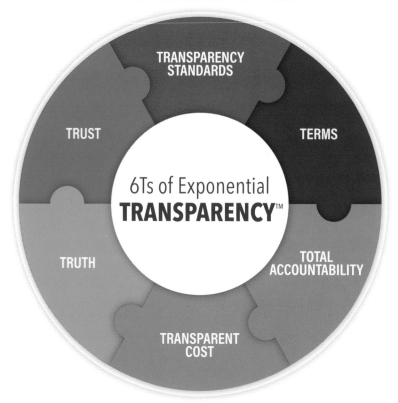

Today, those lessons are not just applied to business, but every aspect of my life.

It is not easy to remove yourself from a situation and view it through someone else's lens. In fact, it might be one of the hardest endeavors you'll ever undertake, but just trying to get to that point is half the battle.

If you can remove your own personal agenda, or at least recognize your preexisting biases, that's a healthy jumpstart toward doing the right thing. It involves being uber-transparent—understanding where you're coming from, where others are coming from, and how those various and divergent paths mesh together. Once you get to that point, it's remarkably easy to see not only where you're coming from, but also the best path or paths going forward.

That may result in some initial or even mid- to long-term discomfort—doing the right thing often does, and for many of us that's especially true when we're putting aside our own financial well-being—but **there's a peacefulness in transparency and purpose that transcends** those issues.

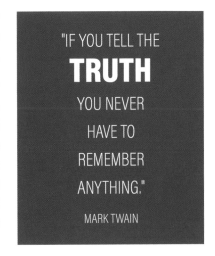

"IF YOU TELL THE **TRUTH** YOU NEVER HAVE TO REMEMBER ANYTHING."

MARK TWAIN

It's a process-driven approach. At 55 years old, I've reached a state of peace. If my satisfaction level with a purpose-driven life is any indication, then I'm looking forward to a long and blissful life.

TRANSPARENCY CHANGES EVERYTHING !!

"**TRUTH IS THE ONLY MEDICINE THAT EVER 'CURES' US**; TRUTH IS THE ONLY MEANS BY WHICH WE CAN LIVE AT OUR FULL, INCREDIBLE POTENTIAL."

BAPTISTE YOGA

pur·pose

/'pərpəs/

the reason for which
something is done or created
or for which something exists.

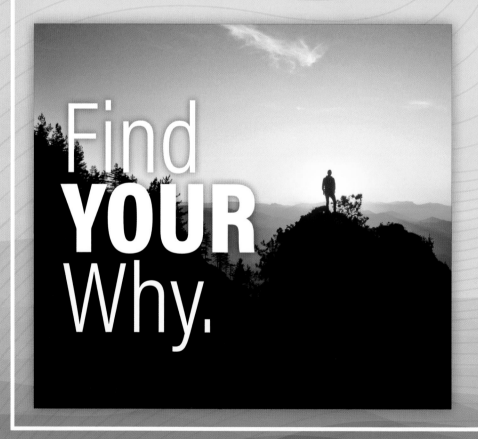

Find **YOUR** Why.

WHY **IT MATTERS:**

- Knowing your sense of purpose is worth seven years of additional life expectancy.

- Success is simple to obtain but requires flawless execution of certain basic principles.

ADVICE:

- Discover your **WHY**.

- Always do the right thing.

- Place others' interests before your own.

TAKE**AWAYS:**

- Transparency equals trust.

- Strive to earn trust in everything you do.

ACTION STEPS**:**

- Always put yourself in a someone else's shoes, especially those of your clients.

- Honor and follow your sense of purpose.

- Have a game plan and be prepared.

"The fastest-growing companies in the world are the most transparent."

Paul Pagnato

TRANSPARENCY WAVE

CHAPTER 20

Financial Crisis

The financial crisis that struck the world in 2008 was the worst of its kind since the Great Depression in 1929.

Over $8 trillion of stock market value was wiped out.

Over $6 trillion of home value was lost.

An estimated ten million Americans lost their homes.

A total of 8.7 million jobs were gone.

Like many people, it changed my life and world view forever.

At the time, I was heading up a Private Banking office in Washington, DC, overseeing a billion dollars of client assets for the largest brokerage firm in the United States. My clients were, and are, powerful people: CEOs, founders of private companies, wealth creators, and ultra-high-net-worth families who had entrusted me with the rewards of their life's work.

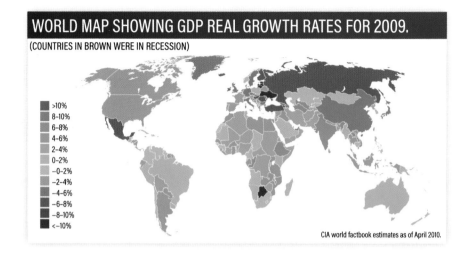

In the years leading up to the financial crisis, I would ask the following question to my clients and prospects: "Do you think the largest brokerage firm in the country could ever go bankrupt?"

Nobody could even conceive of a scenario in which that would happen. Nevertheless, as a result of the financial crisis, the largest brokerage firm in the United States was on the brink of bankruptcy. They were unable to pay bills until the Federal Reserve stepped in and not only bailed the company out by infusing billions of dollars into the company coffers but facilitated a sale to Bank of America.

I started my career in wealth management at Merrill Lynch and over the course of 19 years, learned the market fundamentals from an amazing cadre of mentors. They included: James Hays, who is now the head of Wells Fargo Private Wealth Advisors Group; James Walker, who became the Chief Operating Officer of Credit Suisse; John Thiel, who was Vice Chairman of Bank of America Global Wealth Management & Investment Management; Carl Meyer; who ran the largest brokerage firm office in the country; Raj Sharma, a top-ranked advisor in Boston; Carol Nevins; John Simmons; Riley Etheridge; Phil Blevins; Jack Armstrong; Greg Franks; Tom Fickinger; Louis Chiavacci; Mark Sear; and dozens of others who helped me flourish then, and who now include Dr. Richard Orlando, Jim Schleckser, and Dan Sullivan.

It seemed like everything would go on smoothly forever—but that notion was upended during the financial crisis. Clients' assets were no longer safe. In fact, when companies like Lehman Brothers, Bears Stearns, and Countrywide Financial went under, it was obvious that no asset or institution was safe.

That stress upon the entire financial system and millions of people worldwide exposed fissures and breaking points. It forced us to question the status quo. I was not exempt from that realization. The upheaval led me to question everything and forced me down a deep path of due diligence to understand the types of conflicts that existed in the wealth management industry.

It was not pretty. My examination concluded that there were extensive conflicts between wealth management firms, banks, broker-dealers, insurance companies, and their clients. There was also a substantial amount of non-transparency between advisors and their firms, as well as between advisors and their clients. That realization changed my life forever.

The current wealth management model contained so many conflicts that it could not be saved—not with a Band-Aid or major surgery. The only meaningful path would be to create a new model, stripping out conflicts, providing transparency, and helping ensure safety of assets. This led to the creation and launching of a new company, PagnatoKarp. I overcame any fear of the status quo because of the realization that no other path would be as fulfilling and meaningful.

> **THE ONLY MEANINGFUL PATH** WOULD BE TO CREATE A NEW MODEL, STRIPPING OUT CONFLICTS, PROVIDING **TRANSPARENCY**, AND HELPING ENSURE SAFETY OF ASSETS.

It took three years to craft the ten standards of transparency called True Fiduciary®. This was a holistic effort that involved meetings with SEC commissioners, officials from the Department of Labor, presidents of large wealth management firms, expert attorneys, top regulatory consultants, and my mentors— literally anyone who could provide input on how to create a new model to provide total transparency, removal of conflicts, asset safety, and an entirely new wealth management experience for investors.

By wiping the slate clean, we had freedom to create a new template. It was freeing and invigorating because we could build a model based on clients versus shareholders, focused on purpose versus profits, focused on unleashing value never experienced before in the industry. The energy, positive mental attitude, and fulfillment that we experienced was empowering.

It felt like Tom Brady winning his sixth Super Bowl, an actor winning an Oscar, or a researcher developing a cure for cancer. Sometimes it is still hard to believe that we met our goals.

Of course, it always helps to slide into the perfect era in history. For me, that meant that our efforts coincided with the Transparency Wave and the development of exponential technologies that are disrupting the wealth management industry.

PHOTO CREDIT: "Tom, Feeling the Love"
Flickr photo by David Morris

PagnatoKarp now can provide a plethora of options and choices, ranging from investments, where to place clients' cash, lending rates, unbiased performance reporting, third-party client statements, tax and legal services, financial planning, private banking services, family coaching, and lifestyle services, all following True Fiduciary® standards. With this new model, we have the opportunity to not only compete with the largest banks and wealth management firms in the world, but to increase the value proposition to clients. We created an exponential Breakthrough Value Proposition (BVP) through True Fiduciary® standards of transparency and a True Family Office solution. This has led PagnatoKarp to being named Best Multi-Family Office (New Entrant), Virginia Business Best Places to Work, Top Advisor by Barron's and Forbes, Think Advisor Hall of Fame, and a Financial Times Top RIA,[1] with national media coverage on CNBC, Fox Business News, CNN, The Wall Street Journal and others. And we strive for transparency in every aspect possible.

When employed at a brokerage firm and bank, I always thought I was acting as a fiduciary, but the reality is that structural impediments and incentives prevented me from doing that. That's why advisors at the large wealth management firms are not called "fiduciaries." Allow me to share a few examples of why that's the case.

At most banks and brokerage firms, clients' cash is swept into a proprietary money market account from which the firm profits. At PagnatoKarp, we are forbidden from creating products, holding clients' cash, or sharing in revenues. We place clients' cash in third-party money markets aimed at earning higher rates. That is in the best interests of clients. It's what being a True Fiduciary® is all about.

At most banks and brokerage firms, clients borrow money at whatever rates the firm offers. The firm and advisor both make money from those loans. At PagnatoKarp, we negotiate with the large banks for the best possible rates, and the company and advisors are forbidden from receiving any compensation or kickbacks. This is truly in the best interests of clients.

In that past life, asset management firms would fly us to their offices, pay for luxury hotel rooms, expensive dinners, and tickets to exclusive sporting events. Those firms also had the ability to share in the asset management fees collected from clients. At PagnatoKarp, all of that is forbidden. No airfare, hotel rooms, dinners, or tickets can be provided by an asset management firm. This is all paid for by our firm. We don't permit sharing in asset management fees, either. Once again, this is in the best interests of clients and is the epitome of being a True Fiduciary®.

Previously, when a client purchased a municipal bond or stock, the firm received a commission, known as a markup or spread. At PagnatoKarp, we can solicit widespread bids on the purchase or sale of a security, but we are forbidden from receiving any compensation.

Advisor compensation is so complicated at most banks and brokerage firms, they frequently publish a booklet illustrating all the different ways an advisor receives compensation, and the conflicts are staggering. To help illustrate the effect, the President of the United States mandated a Presidential Study[2] to determine the difference in cost to an investor using a fiduciary versus a traditional broker (aka, "financial advisor"). The results were jaw dropping. It was determined that investors working with a non-fiduciary pay roughly 1% more every year. Over the course of your investing lifetime, that could represent tens or hundreds of thousands of dollars and more.

THE EFFECTS OF CONFLICTED INVESTMENT ADVICE ON RETIREMENT SAVINGS

February 2015

"CONFLICTED ADVICE REDUCES INVESTMENT RETURNS BY ROUGHLY **1% FOR SAVERS.**"

"WE ESTIMATE THE AGGREGATE ANNUAL COST OF CONFLICTED ADVICE IS ABOUT **$17 BILLION EACH YEAR.**"

SOURCE: Page 26, "The Effects Of Conflicted Advice On Retirement Savings", February 2015, The Council of Economic Advisers, within the Executive Office of the President of the United States

The problem goes deeper than the conflicts of interest and deeper than the advisor not being capable of doing the "right thing." The bigger problem is an utter lack of transparency. Clients don't even know all the different ways advisors and their firms are making money from them. The problems are so deeply rooted that most firms are still not capable of providing transparency or being a True Fiduciary®.

> THE PROBLEM GOES DEEPER THAN THE CONFLICTS OF INTEREST AND DEEPER THAN THE ADVISOR NOT BEING CAPABLE OF DOING THE "RIGHT THING."
> **THE BIGGER PROBLEM IS AN UTTER LACK OF TRANSPARENCY.**

The rise of exponential technologies exacerbates and highlights the differences. Previously, we were not capable of providing online transparency and reporting essential information on private investments. Common sense would indicate that clients should always be able to clearly understand each transaction and their current position—how much capital has been called, how much capital they are on the hook for, and what the actual IRR (internal rate of return) is, or how much capital had been distributed by a private investment. That was not possible or easy before. Today, using advanced reporting technology, we can provide this information seamlessly to our clients. That's being a True Fiduciary®.

The old model allows for financial advisors to sell life insurance to their clients. Life insurance sales provide some of the largest upfront commissions to an advisor. There is an incentive for an advisor to sell life insurance products and policies. That means the advisor is not capable of being a True Fiduciary®. What is even worse is the lack of transparency. The client may not clearly understand the commission paid to the advisor or to the advisor's firm. In our True Fiduciary® model, the advisor is forbidden from receiving any compensation from product placements or any commission. The advice given to clients is in their best interests.

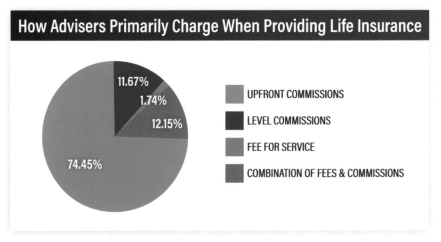

How Advisers Primarily Charge When Providing Life Insurance

- 11.67% — UPFRONT COMMISSIONS
- 1.74% — LEVEL COMMISSIONS
- 12.15% — FEE FOR SERVICE
- 74.45% — COMBINATION OF FEES & COMMISSIONS

SOURCE: Clearview 2019 Adviser Experience Survey

One of the illustrative examples of the tragedies that defined the financial crisis was the Bernie Madoff scheme. Through his misdeeds, investors lost a combined $60 billion. These were affluent and sophisticated investors, including the former CEO of Merrill Lynch, the former NY Attorney General, director Steven Spielberg, actor Kevin Bacon, and the owners of the NY Mets.

MARCH 2009

TRANSPARENCY
TODAY

transparencywave.com

BILLIONAIRE BUSTED

BERNIE MADE-OFF
(OR SO HE THOUGHT)

"I'M SORRY"
SAYS THE $65 BILLION CONMAN

INCLUDING SPECIAL INTERVIEW:
HOW WE WERE RUINED BY BERNIE MADOFF

Bernie Madoff never got caught. After 20 years, he turned himself in when it seemed that the chickens were coming home to roost. How was deception of that magnitude possible? What's even scarier —it's still possible today.

The SEC allowed firms like Bernie Madoff Investment Securities and all the large banks, Wall Street firms, and wealth management firms to engage in the following behaviors that are *not* in clients' best interests. We call these the **"(not so) GREAT EIGHT"**:

THE (NOT SO) GREAT EIGHT

1. CHARGE COMMISSIONS
2. SHARE IN REVENUES WITH ASSET MANAGEMENT FIRMS
3. SHARE IN REVENUES WITH CUSTODIANS
4. SHARE IN REVENUES WITH INSURANCE COMPANIES
5. PROFIT FROM PRODUCTS CREATED
6. GENERATE CLIENT STATEMENTS
7. CALCULATE CLIENT PERFORMANCE RETURNS
8. HOLD CLIENT MONEY

All of these create inherent conflicts and are not in the best interests of the investors. All of these were done by Bernie Madoff, enabling two decades of deceit that was never caught by the regulators. They all still create conflicts and risks for the advisors and clients today.

So why are they allowed?

Profits, nothing else. That's why *all* eight of these "sins" are still allowed today. The regulators have not changed the laws to prohibit these activities. Even after the Bernie Madoff fraud and the financial crisis, nothing has prevented these conflicts on the part of the large banks, broker-dealers, and wealth management firms. At PagnatoKarp, our True Fiduciary® standards forbid us from these conflicted activities. This is the Transparency Wave of the future.

TRANSPARENCY CHANGES EVERYTHING !!

LEGAL TODAY	TRUE FIDUCIARY® MODEL
Charge commissions.	Do **NOT** accept commissions.
Share in revenues with asset management firms.	Receive only one source of revenue: **client fees**.
Share in revenues with custodians.	Remain **independent** from any bank, broker, dealer, insurance or custodian.
Share in revenues with insurance companies.	
Profit from products created.	Do **NOT** create products to sell or price any public securities.
Generate client statements.	Provide fee-only advice.
Calculate client performance returns.	Measure client performance returns using **independent third parties**.
Hold client money.	Do **NOT** hold any client assets, securities or money.

PLUS:

Embrace the legal fiduciary obligation to place **clients' interests first**.

Deliver **comprehensive** financial planning.

Provide **transparency** on portfolios and investments.

Transparency Changes Everything™

WHY **IT MATTERS:**

- The Great Recession of 2009 changed the world forever and taught us many lessons.

- Failures to implement transparency and conflicts leading up to the Great Recession still exist. The responsibility lies on us, the reader and the investor, to reject these conflicts and change the system. We are the ultimate decision makers and vote with our wallets.

ADVICE:

- Ask your financial advisor if they violate any of the "(not so) GREAT EIGHT."

- Always demand full transparency on commissions, kick-backs, and soft-dollar arrangements.

- Never let your advisor calculate your performance returns.

- Never let your advisor hold your assets.

TAKE**AWAYS:**

- Advisor fees and total investment costs are very different—be sure to understand both.

- Digital and robo advisors are not immune to conflicts of interest.

- The Presidential Study[3] concluded the cost difference between a fiduciary advisor and a non-fiduciary advisor is roughly 1% annually.

ACTION STEPS**:**

- Always demand total cost from your advisor. This should include advisor fees, revenue sharing, soft-dollar arrangements, and commissions.

- Seek an independent True Fiduciary® advisor for your financial planning and wealth management needs.

"Transparency
is creating the
greatest wealth
in history and
will continue
to unleash
wealth creation
never seen by
mankind."

Paul Pagnato

CHAPTER 21

Wealth Abundance

More wealth was created in the last ten years than in the entirety of prior human history, and the driving force behind each of the transformative industries has been transparency. A mere 17 companies have collectively created and accumulated a staggering $5 trillion of new wealth, and in each case the "secret sauce" was their relentless focus on bringing transparency to a new level.

In creating that wealth, they certainly bettered themselves, but what makes this massive change so remarkable is that the benefits also accrued to massive numbers of consumers. By enhancing transparency, trust, and simplicity, everyday transactions were simplified and optimized. I believe the Transparency Wave is just beginning and will result in more wealth abundance in the near future than we have ever seen before. New transparency-based industries are now emerging and I am confident a subset of them will unleash new widespread benefits.

These companies—past, present, and future—aren't concentrated in one particular space. Instead, we've seen quantum leaps in diverse fields including artificial intelligence, autonomous vehicles, 3D

> **WE'VE SEEN QUANTUM LEAPS IN DIVERSE FIELDS** INCLUDING ARTIFICIAL INTELLIGENCE, AUTONOMOUS VEHICLES, 3D PRINTING, GENOMIC THERAPIES, MOBILE TRANSACTIONS, ROBOTICS, BLOCKCHAIN, AND DIGITAL ASSETS.

printing, genomic therapies, mobile transactions, robotics, blockchain, and digital assets. While these entities may have diverse areas of expertise, they all rely on advanced technologies to accomplish their goals and improve the user experience. Precisely because they are creating so much value through their ubiquity, they are also advancing transparency—both in their respective industries and throughout the world at large. With that additional transparency, we gain simplicity, trust, and a user experience never seen before.

Take genomic therapies as an example. Historically, most parents would have resisted a requirement that the birth hospital collect and store their newborn child's DNA. They might've feared that the sample could somehow be used against them in the future. Nevertheless, as genomic therapies have advanced, we've reached a tipping point where most new parents can see how greatly the potential advantages outweigh the potential disadvantages. Every state now mandates that all hospital-born babies receive a genomic analysis. In the last two years alone, in just the state of California, those tests determined that over 2,500 babies had abnormalities that could be treated immediately. The results are literally life-changing, and it's all because of genomic transparency.

Another prime example is autonomous vehicles, which provide transparency in transportation. The evidence is clear: today's autonomous vehicles are safer than the average human driver. Nevertheless, there's a constant refrain from the naysayers, when they hear about a Tesla crash, that we shouldn't allow autonomous vehicles on the road. Once again, we've reached a tipping point in our collective understanding, and the numbers don't lie: Tesla sold more

Estimated Crash Rates per Million Miles of Driving With 95% Confidence Intervals

■ Strategic Highway Research Program (SHRP) 2 Overall
□ Self-Driving Car in Autonomous Mode

CAR CRASH RATE PER MILLION MILES

CRASH SEVERITY

Level 1   Level 2   Level 3

SOURCE: "Automated Vehicle Crash Rate Comparison Using Naturalistic Data" Report performed by the Virginia Tech Transportation Institute and commissioned by Google

cars in America than Mercedes Benz in 2018. Why is that the case? It's because Tesla is the safest car on the road today. Car accidents are the second-highest cause of accidental deaths in the United States, claiming lives every day, and over 94% of them are the direct result of human error.

The next time you are in a car, look at how many people are talking, texting, reading, or viewing their PDA devices. Over 90% of drivers use their cell phones for directions and, unfortunately, that can be a fatal decision. Texting is the most alarming distraction. Sending or reading a text takes your eyes off the road for an average of five seconds. Car accidents claimed 1.25 million lives in 2018. That's 3,287 deaths per day. Autonomous vehicles can't be distracted in that way and as a result, they are going to save lives every single day.

Each one of these industries is growing exponentially as a direct result of their conscious decision to ride the Transparency Wave, and in the coming years I fully expect that they will unleash trillions of dollars of new wealth. Cathie Wood, CEO Founder of ARK Investment Management, suggests that each of these industries will grow more than 10x and create an additional cumulative economic value of $12 trillion.

THE ESSENCE OF WEALTH CREATION IS
VALUE CREATION.

Value creation has increased in every wave. From the first wave, the Communication Wave, to the second wave, the Digital Era, and now on to the Transparency Wave, it just grows and grows and grows. The Transparency Wave is going to create more value, I believe, and positively impact more lives than any period human beings have experienced.

My own personal example of wealth creation through transparency is viewed through the prism of PagnatoKarp, when my business partner and I began this journey eight years ago. Prior to that time, I spent 19 years with Merrill Lynch, during which my group accumulated $900 million of assets under advisement. I worked diligently over the course of those 19 years to gain my clients' trust with their assets, but in the subsequent eight-year period, we raised that total to over $4.8 billion in assets under advisement[1] at PagnatoKarp—300% more in less than half the prior period. This all happened without being a large bank or brokerage firm.

How was this possible? The clear answer is that we consciously chose to take transparency in the wealth management industry to a whole new level. We created True Fiduciary® transparency standards to bring simplicity and trust through value creation that elevates the client experience.

The trust factor is accomplished by removing conflicts of interest that existed at our prior firm and that continue to exist throughout most of the industry today. At PagnatoKarp, we are forbidden from receiving any commissions or monetary compensation based on where clients' assets are placed. We don't create any financial products and our clients are provided with an unbiased financial plan. Our only source of revenues are the advisory fees that our clients pay us. Every employee at PagnatoKarp attests to being a True Fiduciary®.

These transparency standards have enabled the company to focus on simplifying the lives of those we serve and creating additional value through services that help streamline complexity. These range from investment, tax, legal, estate, financial planning, and private banking to family coaching, travel, and lifestyle services.

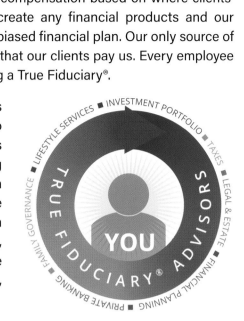

Because we believe so deeply in our transparency standards, the nonprofit True Fiduciary® Institute was launched. The Massive Transformative Purpose (MTP) of the Institute is to positively impact one million lives through transparency and financial literacy. We have created curriculum and are teaching financial education programs at major universities throughout the country, helping strengthen the next generation while fostering tomorrow's leaders. None of this would have been possible without the creation of our transparency standards. None of this would have been possible without following the 6Ts of Exponential Transparency.

TRANSPARENCY CHANGES EVERYTHING !!

PERSPECTIVES

CHAPTER 21 | WEALTH ABUNDANCE

a · bun · dance

/ə'bəndəns/

a very large quantity of something.

Wealth Abundance
ON THE HORIZON !!

WHY **IT MATTERS:**

- The Transparency Wave will create more wealth in the next ten years than in the last hundred. The secret sauce will be with companies focused on exponential transparency, disruptive innovations, and value creation through niche transparency.

ADVICE:

- The opportunity to plan your financial future has never been brighter.
- Follow the 6Ts of Exponential Transparency to help analyze your career path, select a company to work for, and invest your money.

TAKE**AWAYS:**

- Artificial intelligence, autonomous vehicles, 3D printing, genomic therapies, mobile transactions, robotics, blockchain, and digital assets are taking transparency and wealth creation to a whole new level.
- Every newborn child in the United States receives a genomic screening for at least 30 serious conditions.
- 94% of all car accidents are due to human error; texting takes your eyes off the road for an average of five seconds.

ACTION STEPS:

- Take the time to plan your financial future. The next ten years will be one of the greatest wealth-creation opportunities in generations.
- Invest with a long-term horizon in disruptive innovating industries and companies creating a whole new niche of transparency.

"All our dreams can come true, if we have the

COURAGE

to pursue them."

Walt Disney

CHAPTER 22

Transparency Beasts

The Transparency Wave has been fueled by the rise of a group of uber-transparent companies that, in turn, have lit a path for others to follow, building upon their momentum and success. Whether it's a new set of transparency standards, ridiculously simple contract terms or new levels of total accountability, they consistently act in a manner that helps create trust and brand recognition beyond that of their peers.

These transparent unicorns provide such tremendous value and are so unique, they deserve a new name, something reflecting their nature of exponential growth, courage, and leadership. Something that shows their willingness to provide a level of transparency no other company has dared to embrace. This new name needs to fuse fun, purpose and meaning.

We have named them "**Transparency Beasts**".

Many of these companies have done something no other company in their industry has had the courage to do. They've dared to be exponentially transparent and it has rewarded their investors with outsized returns. This is not in spite of the fact that they are exponentially transparent, but **because they are exponentially transparent**. The Transparency Beast companies inside this elite circle also have a passion for impact and place purpose over profits.

Malcom Gladwell is the author of *Outliers*, a best-selling book and one of the largest studies of exceptional people operating at the extreme outer edge of what

is statistically plausible. Gladwell explains that reaching the 10,000-hour rule is a key to success in any field, and a matter of practicing a specific task 20 hours a week for 10 years.

Well, it is safe to say that over the last 27 years, I have far exceeded Malcolm Gladwell's 10,000-hour mark in my efforts to analyze companies and the portfolio managers buying the stocks of those companies. I have had the unique opportunity to speak with hundreds of portfolio managers, superstars ranging from pure bond managers, like Bill Gross, Mohamed El-Erian and Jeffrey Gundlach, to pure stock managers, like Warren Buffet, Charlie Munger, Bill Miller, and Peter Lynch, to private equity gurus like David Rubinstein and venture capitalist Vinod Khosla.

It is apparent that a key common denominator to their successes has been their ability to blend both quantitative and qualitative analysis into their results. In our search for Transparency Beast companies, we applied both types of analysis to the 6Ts of Exponential Transparency– Transparency Standards, Terms, Total Accountability, Transparent Cost, Truth and Trust. Companies scoring highly on each marker put them in the upper echelons of transparency and helped identify those demonstrating the six core qualities.

A mentor and friend of mine, Daniel Pink, is the #1 New York Times best-selling author of multiple groundbreaking books about business, work, and behavior, including *When*, *To Sell is Human*, *Drive* and *A Whole New Mind*. Pink is extremely transparent and helped me crystalize this process. Surprisingly, it didn't happen in a boardroom or at a seminar but, rather, while attending a Washington Nationals baseball game with our wives.

It was an incredible game with a variety of numerical milestones. The Nationals' pitcher recorded a stunning 14 strikeouts and two of the Nationals' star hitters hit their 30th home runs of the season on route to a 7-0 victory. As we watched this sublime performance, the magical moment came when Dan suggested creating a Transparency Index to demonstrate how companies harness transparency to help outperform their peers.

GUESS WHAT? **IT'S BEING CREATED!**

Since that night, I have been on a single-minded path to create a numerical explanation of my hypotheses. The result is **a Transparency Stock Index which tracks companies demonstrating the highest levels of transparency**. The goal of the Index is to help promote higher transparency awareness, new investor opportunities, increased accountability, and an incentive for all companies to integrate transparency throughout their businesses.

A profound thanks to Daniel Pink for the magical moment and provocative thoughts for creating a Transparency Stock Index.

The next step was to find the most comprehensive research performed on the relationship between transparency and corporate earnings. The most widely-cited paper, entitled "Cost of Capital Earnings Transparency"[1], was written by three PhDs from Stanford Business School and published in the Journal of Accounting and Economics. The research culminated with a 200-page paper and sophisticated algorithm analyzing the earnings transparency of publicly traded companies. The conclusion was that companies with more transparent earnings have a lower cost of capital and, therefore, superior earnings than their peers.

Author Yaniv Konchitchki agreed to meet with me and share his findings. Yaniv received his PhD in Business Administration and MSc in Statistics from Stanford's Graduate School of Business. He also holds a CPA license and is a military special forces veteran. Yaniv is now a professor at University of California at Berkeley's Haas School of Business.

According to Professor Konchitchki, the importance of transparency in the real world is notable when considering the U.S. capital markets, as reflected from recent cutting-edge research. Specifically, a recent research study demonstrates that greater transparency in corporate earnings has a positive effect on the bottom line, thus making a case for more transparent financial information provided by Corporate America.

The research, entitled "Cost of Capital Earnings Transparency"[1] and published in the Journal of Accounting and Economics, was co-authored by Professors Yaniv Konchitchki (University of California at Berkeley's Haas School of Business), Mary Barth (Stanford University's Graduate School of Business) and Wayne Landsman (University of North Carolina at Chapel Hill's Kenan-Flagler Business School). It focuses on the linkage between the transparency of a corporate's financial statements and its discount rate (also called "cost of equity capital").

The paper provides theory and finds evidence that U.S. corporations with more transparent accounting earnings information enjoy higher stock valuations (through lower discount rates). More specifically, "a corporate's value is often determined by discounting future cash flows by the corporate's cost of capital." Cost of capital is defined as the rate of return that capital could be expected to earn in an alternative investment of equivalent risk. It is used to evaluate new projects within a company to give investors information and assurance of a minimum return for providing capital.

The research finds that a corporate's cost of capital is negatively related to its financial transparency. In other words, when there is less earnings transparency, the risk to investors is higher, resulting in higher cost of capital. Likewise, if there is more earnings transparency, one has access to more information about a company's value by observing its earnings, resulting in lower risk and, in turn, lower cost of capital. Ultimately, lower cost of capital equates to higher valuation of a firm's stocks.

The research also provides two notable innovations. One is that this study was the first to provide an economic mechanism that directly links an empirical accounting quality measure to cost of capital, through the channel of information asymmetry -- an important contribution to the research literature. The second innovation uses cost of capital measures that are not affected by common biases such as those stemming from using growth forecasts or analyst earnings forecasts to derive implied cost of capital measures that were often used in the literature. This paper was recently selected as the Best Paper Award by the American Accounting Association, "judged to best reflect the tradition of academic scholarship and be of relevance to problems facing the accounting profession and standard-setters," as quoted by this award.

This research changes how we consider the quality of financial data from corporate financial statements, because the evidence in this paper illuminates how important transparent accounting is for stock valuation. -- Professor Yaniv Konchitchki

To create the Transparency Stock Index, the top Russell 1000 publicly traded companies in the United States were analyzed. The goal was to cast a wide net to capture as much data as possible on a large group of companies. Both qualitative and quantitative characteristics were then incorporated, the essential keys to successfully identifying Transparency Stock Index constituents.

The qualitative research applied the 6Ts of Exponential Transparency to an in-depth analysis encompassing consumer reports on brand loyalty, lawsuits filed, transparency standards created, 10K and 10Q public filings, and annual reports. The quantitative analysis focused on earnings transparency and utilized the algorithm created and published by the Stanford PhD authors in the "Cost of Capital Earnings Transparency".

Google (Alphabet Inc.) is a great example of a company who demonstrated both qualitative and quantitative aspects of the Transparency Stock Index. Qualitatively, Google exemplifies the sixth T, TRUST, through their use of information transparency. Quantitatively, their earnings transparency for 2018 was 42% when applied to the Stanford algorithm (see Appendix 1 for data metrics), illuminating shareholder value that was considerably higher than the overall market return of the Russell 1000 for the same time period.

TRANSPARENCY BEAST

COMPANIES APPLYING THE 6Ts

1. TRANSPARENCY STANDARDS	2. TERMS	3. TOTAL ACCOUNTABILITY
Easy-to-understand rules leading to high levels of transparency.	Ridiculously simple customer contract.	High quality governance. Definable consequences. Adherence to standards & terms.
★ APPLE PRIVACY STANDARDS	★ UBER RIDE-SHARING TRANSPARENCY	★ WHOLE FOODS VENDOR TRANSPARENCY
★ SQUARE RESPONSIBLE TRANSPARENCY	★ TESLA COST TRANSPARENCY, AUTONOMOUS DRIVING TRANSPARENCY	★ PATAGONIA SUPPLY CHAIN TRANSPARENCY
★ AMGEN DISCLOSURE TRANSPARENCY	★ T-MOBILE VALUE TRANSPARENCY	★ LULULEMON SUPPLY CHAIN TRANSPARENCY
★ BAXTER POLICY TRANSPARENCY	★ TWITTER TRANSPARENT EXCHANGE OF INFORMATION, TRANSPARENCY REPORT	★ BRIDGEWATER RADICAL TRANSPARENCY
★ CONAGRA BRANDS SUSTAINABILITY COMMITMENT	★ SOUTHWEST FARE TRANSPARENCY	★ NASDAQ MARKET TRANSPARENCY

The illustration below highlights some Transparency Beast companies and how they demonstrate alignment with the 6Ts of Exponential Transparency. Companies executing on all 6 tiers are considered to be exponentially transparent, with the highest levels of value, brand loyalty and employee satisfaction. As you consider the data, reflect on how you can unleash a new wave of transparency through the 6Ts. If your company is not being this transparent, you're already behind the eight ball.

TRANSPARENCY CHANGES EVERYTHING !!

4. TRANSPARENT COST	5. TRUTH	6. TRUST
Accurate and total cost. No hidden fees. Easy to understand.	Communicating facts openly and accurately. Data-based communication.	Complete consumer loyalty. Exponential transparency.
★ AMAZON COST TRANSPARENCY	★ STARBUCKS CULTURE AND SALARY TRANSPARENCY	★ DISNEY CULTURAL TRANSPARENCY
★ COSTCO COST TRANSPARENCY	★ VISA NETWORK TRANSPARENCY	★ GOOGLE INFORMATION TRANSPARENCY
★ AIRBNB COST TRANSPARENCY	★ SALESFORCE DATA TRANSPARENCY	★ DOCUSIGN ESIGNATURE TRUST, PAY TRANSPARENCY
★ WALMART COST TRANSPARENCY	★ PAYPAL PAYMENT TRANSPARENCY, VENMO	★ MICROSOFT AI TRANSPARENCY, OPEN SOURCE TRANSPARENCY
★ SPOTIFY COST TRANSPARENCY	★ NETFLIX STREAMING VIDEO TRANSPARENCY, RADICAL TRANSPARENCY	★ FIDELITY INVESTMENT TRANSPARENCY
		★ VANGUARD FEE TRANSPARENCY

PERSPECTIVES

CHAPTER 22 I TRANSPARENCY BEASTS

beast
/bēst/

a term applied to those seen
as bigger than life or more
commanding of respect
in their field.

IS YOUR COMPANY A
TRANSPARENCY BEAST?

WHY **IT MATTERS:**

- Historical data shows that companies reporting transparent earnings and incorporating the 6Ts unleash value for their shareholders while enjoying higher brand loyalty and a superior company culture.

ADVICE:

- Always consider qualitative and quantitative data when doing research.
- Companies not being transparent are already behind the eight ball.
- Read *To Sell is Human*, by Daniel Pink.

TAKE**AWAYS:**

- Transparency Beast companies have created over $5 trillion of new wealth in the last ten years.
- The truth is in the data.
- Uber-transparent companies have lit a path for others to follow.
- Transparency Beast companies are demonstrating the 6Ts of Exponential Transparency.

ACTION STEPS:

- Practice the 10,000-hour rule as a key to success.
- Find the companies that have a passion for impact and place purpose over profits.
- Innovate to unleash transparency at a whole new level.

"THE ONLY THING WE HAVE TO
FEAR IS FEAR ITSELF."

FRANKLIN DELANO ROOSEVELT

CHAPTER 23

Personal Transparency

When it comes to integrating and maximizing transparency in your life, the hardest and highest hurdles to surmount often involve personal transparency. Fear is a driving force in most of our lives, with an evolutionary pedigree dating back thousands of years. Finding the willpower and the means to break through this perceived ceiling opens exponential opportunities.

One of my most life-altering experiences occurred at a week-long yoga teacher training in Sedona, Arizona in 2016. Approximately 100 of us spent a week unplugged—no cell phones, laptops, texts, or emails— just pure yoga. I expected physical transformation as a result of this process, and that certainly ensued, but my greatest realizations involved personal inquiries, which I now know enabled and emboldened my sense of personal transparency.

The group in attendance from all over the world were largely physically fit, with great positive mental attitudes. They were well aware of the fundamentals of yoga, the poses, and the origins. The days were intense, starting at 7 a.m. and lasting past 10 p.m. I presume it was similar in many ways to the training given to Navy Seals, designed to break us down and then build us back up, and the focus on personal inquiries snowballed each day as well. By the halfway mark, all of us were physically and mentally exhausted. The instructor asked us to pair up with someone we had never met before and share the #1 obstacle facing us. At a time when we were completely physically and mentally exhausted, we had to share our most significant challenges. We had little strength for masquerade or subterfuge, and that led to utter transparency. Everyone felt that they were in a safe place, and despite meeting with a complete stranger, nobody had an agenda. After 30 minutes of emotional transparency, we were asked to share our obstacles with the group.

Twenty people, one by one, got up in front of the entire group and provided complete transparency on their main issue. Each person started with the circumstance and then ended with the obstacle they were facing. I teared up listening to what people had been through and the problems they were dealing with. The issues ranged from being victims of rape and abuse to marital infidelity to being stuck in long-term relationships with partners they didn't love or even like.

Guess what all 20 people said the "real" problem was?

Whether the obstacle was to overcome the trauma of abuse or a relationship they no longer wanted to be part of, the problem was them, not the other person. Not the person who abused and raped them. Not the person damaging the long-term relationship they remained in.

One by one, all 20 people exercised the true courage to speak up in front of the entire group. The lesson learned was that no matter what the problem facing us, we were the only ones who had the power to move past it.

We are our own obstacle, and the only way to move forward is to take action. We can't rely on others to do so. This all starts with personal transparency and identifying and accepting core issues. Once we reconcile with the truth, we need to be transparent with others.

A few years ago, my son was struggling and transparently shared with the family the obstacles he was facing. He demonstrated great strength in honestly identifying what was holding him back. His strength led the family to seek counseling from a third party.

The counselor's conclusion was something that I would never have expected in a million years: he stated that I was a significant part of the problem. My behavior enabled my son's harmful behaviors and therefore prevented him from overcoming the obstacles that he faced.

I was simultaneously shocked and relieved. I thought that I'd been helping him and never would have thought my actions were harmful, yet I was relieved that now I was free to take steps in the right direction. It took that third party to help me be more transparent with myself and other family members. Anyone with children knows how difficult it can be to balance providing opportunities and providing tough love.

WE ARE OUR OWN OBSTACLE, AND THE ONLY WAY TO MOVE FORWARD IS TO TAKE ACTION.

My advice is to throw fear out the window when you find yourself in a similar situation. Share your true thoughts, feelings, and circumstances with the ones you love and those who might be impacted. My son is thriving now and in the best place he's been in years.

The value of personal transparency extends to businesses, as well. Often businesses start when two or more people with complementary skill sets realize that combining their talents provides tremendous leverage—they're more than the sum of their parts. Even when that's the case, however, the fact is that 90% of partnerships fail.

I've been in a business partnership for over 20 years. We've defied the odds because we recognize and embrace each other's purposes and differences.

My primary motivation is making a difference to people, the community, and society. Our company's Massive Transformative Purpose (MTP), of positively impacting one million lives through standards of transparency, is what gets me out of bed and motivates me every day. In case you can't tell, the glass is always half full for me. I'm always looking to turn a negative into a positive. My go-to quotes are "The first negative thought is a thought to failure" and "Success is failure turned inside out."

While I've been fortunate to experience financial success, money has never motivated me. I've seen and experienced the negative impacts that money's trappings have on people and relationships over the years. In fact, it has ruined relationships in my own family. I don't shun it. On the contrary, to me money is simply a tool to create value and help people.

My business partner of 20 years couldn't be more different than me. His glass is often half empty, and his focus is on what can go wrong versus the existing opportunities. For him, the primary goal of business is profit, not purpose, and he works extremely hard to provide a good quality life for his family. One of his favorite sayings is, "Don't give me a problem, provide me the solution."

As you could imagine, such inherently different world views could cause substantial friction and conflict between two partners. So how has our partnership survived for over 20 years?

THE ANSWER: TRANSPARENCY.

We both are completely transparent with one another. We push one another. We challenge one another. We find compromise. Most successful businesses have a balance between profits and purpose. The cofounder of Whole Foods, John Mackey, wrote a tremendous book called *Conscious Capitalism*. In it, he explained that profits are essential for sustainability, which in turn allows a business's purpose to be carried out and fulfilled. My partner and I know exactly where each of us stands on all issues. There are no surprises and that would not be possible without uber-transparency.

My business serving ultra-high-net-worth individuals has flourished for over two decades because our core philosophy is to tell high-net-worth individuals what they need to hear versus what they want to hear. Our clients typically have incredibly persuasive personalities. They often employ hundreds or even thousands of employees, and they're responsible for millions or even billions of dollars in revenue. Our legal obligation as a True Fiduciary® is to always do what is in our clients' best interests. That means always providing transparency. Sometimes this means walking away from potential new business opportunities, the type of opportunities that would make the career of another financial advisor.

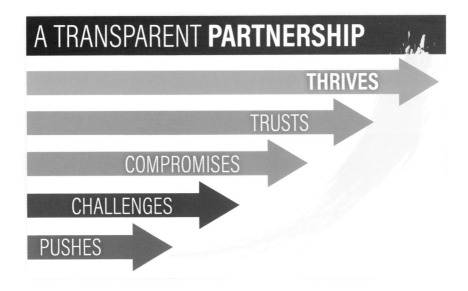

> MOST SUCCESSFUL BUSINESSES HAVE A BALANCE BETWEEN
> **PROFITS AND PURPOSE.**

Let me share a real-life example. One of the most successful entrepreneurs in the DC metropolitan area was referred to us by his attorney of 30 years. He'd already met with every other major wealth management firm and bank in the area and as we discussed his goals, he shared his risk tolerance and the return he expected from the portfolio.

A few years earlier, this gentleman had lost $60 million with Bernie Madoff, so was focused on our firm with True Fiduciary® standards of transparency. When he concluded the interview process, he called me to share that he'd selected our company. This would have been a significant relationship with substantial fees.

Unfortunately, we had to decline his business. His return expectations were simply too high. As you could imagine, this upset him; he wasn't used to anyone saying "no" to him.

Six months later, he called again. He was chastened and admitted that his return expectations had been too high. He wanted to reassess and follow a more realistic path. He's now been a great client for over a decade, but we could not have built this successful relationship if we didn't tell him what he *needed* to hear from the very start. If we'd just told him what he *wanted* to hear, we would likely have had a very disappointed client.

Another example that might shock a lot of people occurred at the height of the financial crisis. Lehman Brothers collapsed, Bear Stearns went out of business, Countrywide Mortgage went under, and nobody knew which financial giant would go under next or when.

The Dow had dropped 777 points, the largest single day drop in history. Guess what we were doing that day? We were calling our clients and making the largest stock purchases of the year. That wasn't the advice that our powerful clients wanted to hear. They wanted us to tell them to sell everything and go primarily into cash until the market sell-off stopped. We were telling them to do just the opposite—buy stocks with cash.

That's human nature. We have been taught since we were little not to touch the stove when it's hot. We are trained to avoid risk, danger, and uncertainty. That's fine, but typically the best way to make money in stocks is to buy low and hold on for a long time. A stock is typically the lowest when nobody wants to buy it, when there is a lot of uncertainty, when fear is in the market. That's exactly what we were doing—buying low, when fear and uncertainty were very high. It took tremendous courage, and we conveyed the facts transparently to our clients. One of Warren Buffett's most widely cited quotations makes this point succinctly: "Be fearful when others are greedy, and greedy when others are fearful."

Our business growth is 100% organic. We don't buy other advisors' clients. Instead, we accrue them through client referrals, centers of influence referrals, reputation, brand recognition, and people searching for a boutique firm serving CEO Founders. Most of the people who interview us end up becoming clients. On the rare occasions when

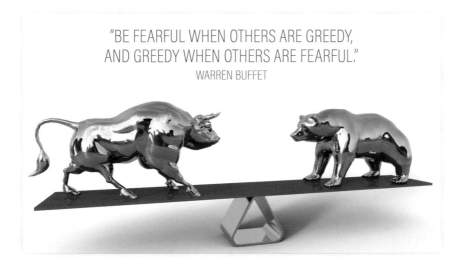

"BE FEARFUL WHEN OTHERS ARE GREEDY, AND GREEDY WHEN OTHERS ARE FEARFUL."
WARREN BUFFET

they demur, the reasoning is usually based on price transparency. We provide complete transparency on all the real costs for Intelligent Wealth Management™ at PagnatoKarp: the cost of portfolio management, tax preparation and compliance, legal services, banking services, concierge services, and family counseling. Every CEO Founder needs these services, and they're included in our fee structure.

Meanwhile, other advisors quote only the advisor fee, and it typically comes in lower. What's not stated is what isn't included: asset management costs, custodial costs, and all the other related services. When they receive the bill, the client is often shocked to see that it's far, far higher than expected. This dynamic ultimately leads to distrust. It's similar to what happens in the real estate industry. A home may be for sale for $500,000, but when you factor in the closing costs, real estate commissions, title insurance, and other fees, the bottom line is often closer to $550,000. The companies that provide complete fee transparency will likely flourish and those that don't are doomed to go out of business.

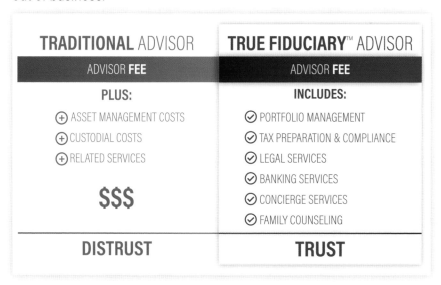

One of my favorite pastimes is collective goal setting and sharing, but most people are very uncomfortable transparently sharing their goals. They don't have to be monumental aspirations, but rather something about relationships, health, professions, or academic endeavors.

Whether they're big or small, the primary reason many people resist sharing their goals is fear of failure. It's a fear that others might hold them accountable.

A classic example of this are New Year's resolutions. On January 1, many people desire a new start and millions of them define and articulate their aspirations. Unfortunately, most of them never achieve those goals. According to *U.S. News and World Report*, an overwhelming 80% of New Year's resolutions go unfulfilled.[1]

Why? I believe it's because they don't write them down or share them with other people. That means there is no accountability. Furthermore, they don't have the positive encouragement of others to push them.

I create goals every year, not exclusively on January 1, but throughout the year. They change constantly, sometimes because I've achieved the goals and other times because they're moot or may be surpassed by something to which I've given a higher priority.

My goals are broken into four segments, a structure that provides guardrails to help maintain a balanced life. Here are my four segments:

1. HEALTH
   nutrition, cardiovascular soundness, mental health, and IQ.

2. RELATIONSHIPS
   family, peers, team, mentors, friends, and travel experiences.

3. SPIRITUAL
   community, meditation, prayer, and nonprofit endeavors.

4. PROFESSIONAL
   businesses, investments, boards, and mentoring.

As you can see, there is a lot going on.

A goal without a plan is just a wish !!

All my goals are shared with all immediate family members, company, mentors, and close friends. Openly sharing goals forces clarity, focus, and accountability.

This has inadvertently developed into an annual ritual. Every year, interested people ask me for a list of my goals. In turn, the process helps them create and think for themselves.

I've been inspired by a quotation by J.K. Rowling: "It is impossible to live without failing at something unless you live so cautiously that you might as well have not lived at all."

People get excited when setting goals; people are excited to start the new year. Making a small tweak of transparently sharing your written goals will help you move out of the 80% who don't consistently achieve to the 20% who do.

The reasons so many people never overcome the obstacles in front of them, pursue their dreams, discover their unique abilities, or spend the majority of their day on things they love or with the people they love are because to do so would require a wholesale change in habits and attitude. There are various ways to get to that next level—it's not a one-size-fits-all solution—but I'm confident that any successful path will incorporate the following six elements.

TRANSPARENCY CHANGES EVERYTHING !!

SIX STEPS TO **PERSONAL TRANSPARENCY**:

1. **RELEASE**

    Release the things on your mind that are preventing you from moving forward, the negative mental chatter that's holding you back. If you can honestly visualize and memorialize the positive thoughts, you'll have a better sense of the real you, the one who will be happiest and most fulfilled.

2. **FEARS**

    Block out the noise and get *real* with the personal fears you are facing. What is getting in your way? Identifying the obstacles is the first step in determining what should no longer be acceptable to you, thereby unleashing your energy and creativity, and setting you on the road to your dreams and happiness.

3. **FOCUS**

    Identify the #1 action needed to overcome your personal fears and put it front and center. If there's a step you need to take, or a conversation that can't wait any longer, make it happen as soon as possible.

4. **POSITIVITY**

    Figure out the benefits that you will receive, and how you'll help others flourish, by overcoming your personal fear. You'll probably be surprised at how far-ranging the impacts may be.

5. **STORY**

    Compile your inspirations in the form of a *story*. It needn't be pure narrative— different people express and create differently. Some of us love to draw, some love to write, some love to talk, some love to walk and talk. Create your story in your own preferred medium, the one that provides you with the greatest energy.

6. **SHARE**

    Share your story with people you love as often as possible. The more you share, the more real it will become, and the more accountable you'll feel to yourself and others.

CHAPTER 23 I PERSONAL TRANSPARENCY

goal

/gōl/

the object of a person's ambition or
effort; an aim or desired result.

Openly sharing goals forces clarity, focus, and accountability.

PROFESSIONAL - HEALTH - RELATIONSHIPS - SPIRITUAL -

GOALS

WHY **IT MATTERS:**

- The #1 real obstacle for all humans is personal fear. If you put your mind to it, there is no fear that cannot be overcome. Tackle your fears head-on through transparency, and it can be surprising how quickly your perceived problems will melt away.

ADVICE:

- When faced with an obstacle, don't act hastily. Take the time necessary to gain clarity on the obstacle preventing your breakthrough.

- Share your story with as many people as possible.

TAKE**AWAYS:**

- Conscious capitalism provides a balance of purpose and profits.

- "Be fearful when others are greedy and greedy when others are fearful." – Warren Buffett

- 80% of New Year's resolutions fail.

- We are what we think; we are what we say.

ACTION STEPS**:**

- Break down your goals into four categories—health, relationships, spiritual, and professional.

- Engage the 6Ts of Personal Transparency: Release, Fears, Focus, Positivity, Story, Share.

"In a gentle way,
you can shake the world."

Mahatma Gandhi

TRANSPARENCY WAVE

CHAPTER 24

Transparency Culture

Every entity, from the smallest to the largest, can attain its maximum effectiveness by implementing transparency culture into its structure. Don't take my word for it—many of the world's greatest corporate leaders, philanthropists, and other leading thinkers have made this a priority. They've sought to help others flourish in this manner and, in turn, they've seen their own success grow exponentially.

One personal example of this phenomenon hit home when my wife and I attended a fundraiser to fight the effects of Alzheimer's disease. This cause has become a huge passion of mine, largely because I've seen loved ones suffer through its ill effects. Current models indicate that once you pass 80 years old, you have a 50% chance of developing Alzheimer's or some similar sort of debilitating dementia. It tears families apart as they see their family members suffer, and it also challenges the caretakers.

Because of my concern over these issues, I was committed to making a sizable donation before we even got there, but once arrived, had an opportunity to do even more. Howard Schultz, the former CEO of Starbucks and former owner of the Seattle Supersonics, is also passionate about battling this nefarious disease. In order to goose the bidding, he offered up a dinner with him to the highest bidder. Even without the underlying cause, I would've relished the chance to dine with him. He had been a visionary business leader and had inextricably woven coffee into the fibers of our country's culture while building one of the world's biggest brands.

In the end, we were very fortunate to have won the bidding process and were set to have dinner with Howard Schultz. The date finally arrived and in preparation, studied all press clippings and everything publicly available on Starbucks and Mr. Schultz. This culminated with a list of questions for the epic dinner we were about to have. Heading into something like that, you always wonder if you'll hit it off with the other party. Schultz turned out to be a delightful, kind, and thoughtful human being. He was down to earth, too, and gushed at length about the various New York sports teams, including his beloved Giants.

Right off the bat, started with the heavy-hitting questions: "What keeps you up at night?"

Desirous of getting to the root of focus for one of the world's most successful entrepreneurs. What was his top concern?

The question had barely left my mouth when he started his reply without the slightest hesitation: "Culture."

He was convinced—and I'm sure that he remains convinced—that for Starbucks or any business, the most important thing is the people. Without the people, a business has nothing. One of the ways he internalized this is that he never refers to the people who work with him as "employees." Instead, they are "partners." That simple verbiage alters relationships and mindsets. It leads to a culture of inclusion. Every full-time "partner" enjoys benefits and equity. Whether you're in the corporate jet or taking out the trash, everyone is respected and valued. Perhaps most importantly from my point of view, everyone is treated warmly and with transparency, dignity, and respect.

That dinner with Howard Schultz contributed to advancing the culture of transparency that we have created at PagnatoKarp. We are employee-owned. Every full-time "partner" has units in the company.

We are structured as a partnership with limited or no upward restraints—any employee has the opportunity to pursue any job opening or career path. We refer to employees as "team members" to cultivate an ethos of teamwork in all that we do.

This feeling isn't just limited to internal office operations. Each family office client has a dedicated team, as opposed to other firms where they might work exclusively with one advisor. The team typically consists of a planner, attorney, portfolio manager, tax advisor and CPA, concierge, family counselor, and a private banker. You have someone at your beck and call at all times with deep expertise in the area that needs attention. We are constantly focused on maximizing service and creating value for our clients.

How do we keep team members excited about the ultimate goal? One way is to ensure that their levels of energy, creativity, and focus

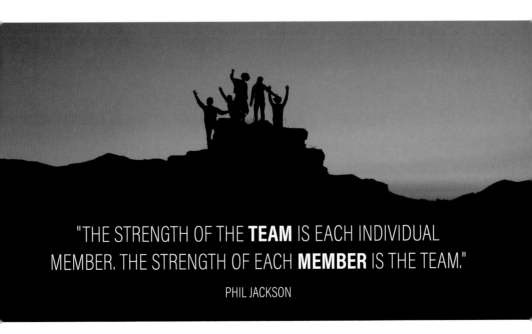

"THE STRENGTH OF THE **TEAM** IS EACH INDIVIDUAL MEMBER. THE STRENGTH OF EACH **MEMBER** IS THE TEAM."

PHIL JACKSON

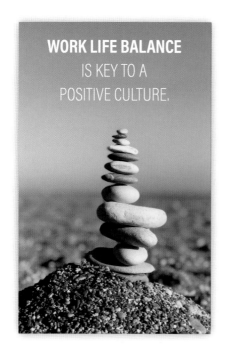

WORK LIFE BALANCE IS KEY TO A POSITIVE CULTURE.

are on point. That means after a demanding period of work, they need to be rejuvenated—so every team member receives one full week off every quarter, plus a day off for their birthday and multiple days off to serve our community. The message we're sending is that you, the team member, are important to us and to our clients, and to our community, and we want to help you be in tip-top shape.

We also have learning days—programs dedicated entirely to learning something (or several things). We've invited a top neuroscientist, world-renowned nutritionist, and motivational speakers from the Dale Carnegie Institute to address our assembled team. We've also structured programs around "Designing a Better Business," issues related to longevity, portfolio management, blockchain, and reading days. Keeping with the democratic and team-oriented approach, the team selects topics they would like to learn about.

The principal motivation for founding our company was to bring transparency into the financial industry. With our Massive Transformative Purpose to positively impact one million lives through standards of transparency, we live and breathe transparency every single day.

Once a quarter we have "Company Day." We often spend half the day serving the community and half the day improving ourselves and the business. The program involves an open accounting of the company's financials, revenues, earnings, and margins. We clearly spell out what our goals were for the quarter and talk extensively about what worked and didn't work. Every section of the business goes through this process as a reflection of striving for total transparency.

In a departure from most corporate environments, we fully expect every team member to engage in some sort of experimentation every quarter. The more experiments we have, the more failures we have. With that out of the way, we are well on our way to success. Team members transparently share their experiments, without fear of censure or retribution. Whether it resulted in a success or failure, or somewhere in between, it's part of a constant effort to unleash new value for our clients. This has repeatedly resulted in new investment opportunities, enhanced performance, access to new technologies, or brand-new services.

Our hiring process is thorough and lengthy so we're sure we provide prospective employees with transparency on how we operate and our expectations for team members. Meanwhile, it provides us with clarity on the new hire—everything from salary needs to preferred modes of communication to career goals. We know that our team members are more than what they do inside our office space, so we endeavor to learn about their families and hobbies, along with their value systems. If we can fully understand what gives them energy and what causes them conflict and stress, it makes us a better team. None of this would be possible without transparency and that starts with us, PagnatoKarp.

We put potential hires through a heavy series of meetings, bringing them in front of as many team members as possible, so they understand the people they will be working with, not just their direct line of command.

A TRANSPARENCY **TEAM**

T	E	A	M
TEACHES	EXPERIMENTS	ASSESSES	MENTORS

+ EMPOWERS, ENCOURAGES, ENGAGES & **EXCELS!**

Each additional meeting, phone call, and email provides us with more data points, all which factor into our decision process.

Candidates are required to read the best-seller Exponential Organizations by Salim Ismail. This serves two purposes: First, it allows us to learn how they assess information and then apply it to our company. Second, because our company strives to be an exponential organization, this provides them with further insight into our corporate DNA. If they read the book thoughtfully and carefully, they'll leave with clearer expectations related to our culture, systems, and processes.

We also require candidates to present a project, and it need not have anything to do with their potential position. This allows us to interact with the candidate in an entirely different manner. We want to see them in action, presenting to a group. This often lets us know if they'll be adequately transparent with team members, clients, the marketplace, and regulators.

Our consistent goal is to lead by example, and I'm proud of the fact that I frequently receive calls from other advisors asking for advice. They are often shocked when I invite them to visit our offices, meet with any team member, and let them ask any question they would like. We are open and transparent.

One of our core transparency principles is a concept called "unique ability." Kathy Kolbe, one of the world's leading experts on human instincts, created a survey that provides transparency on anyone's unique ability. Every team member is required to complete this survey before joining PagnatoKarp. We want to fully understand their passions, which aides us in assessing if they are in line with the role they would have at PagnatoKarp. We strive for each person to spend 80% of their day making the most of their unique ability.

Despite initial impressions and preferences, life is a journey and all of us constantly grow, personally and professionally. Thus, we have found that it can be completely normal for someone to join the company with a passion for a certain role and then see that passion evolve or change over time. We have a responsibility as an organization to recognize this. If we're in tune with those changes, we can help the team member and help ourselves. In some instances, this means our company is no longer the optimal place for them to pursue their goals or dreams. Rather than regretting that separation, we take pride and joy in watching a human being develop and grow personally and professionally.

I am currently helping a former team member transition to another career path in another industry. That tells me that our culture of transparency is working. Without it, we would not be able to help this person move forward and become fulfilled while maximizing their impact on society. They might be non-transparently searching for another position. This team member has been with us for years, adding tremendous value to our clients and the organization along the way. I have personally mentored this individual, and while some would take their departure as a slap in the face, I see it the other way. It would have been tragic not to be able to help.

"EVERY COMPANY
HAS A PROBLEM
WITH ITS INTERNAL
IMMUNE SYSTEM
FIGHTING DISRUPTIVE
INNOVATION."

SALIM ISMAIL
BEST-SELLING AUTHOR,
EXPONENTIAL ORGANIZATIONS

Within our various office spaces, we take great pains to ensure physical transparency. Our architectural hallmarks include large open spaces, huge windows, and complete glass for offices and conference rooms. All offices have separation between the glass to ensure open transparency. Every team meeting is open to everyone in the company—in fact, we encourage all to attend our investment committee meetings, learning days, and client meetings. This uber-inclusiveness is about seeking the flourishing of others.

A critical part of maximizing organizational transparency is to avoid a top-down hierarchy. In other words, transparency and decentralization go hand in hand. As the CEO Founder of PagnatoKarp, I've wrestled with this reality on multiple occasions. It is not always easy to empower others to make decisions. No one wants to let a team member down, so inevitably there's a fear of failure, a fear of disappointing another team member. We hire the best of the best, true "A" players, and they bring passion to work every day. They're not used to failing. What I have learned over the years is that in order to maximize outcomes, I must empower others to make decisions, including big decisions. If I want to make that truly effective, it's critical that I remove myself completely from the entire decision-making process. The more removed, the more empowered others are. This has helped me transition our company from being top-down to bottom-up. It has taken us on a path from centralized to decentralized decision-making. I would be lying if I said this wasn't uncomfortable at first. Indeed, change by its very nature is uncomfortable. Nevertheless, this step is essential for any organization to be truly transparent.

Year after year, we are listed as one of the best places to work by prominent organizations. The true proof is in the pudding, though—we see that we are far outside the industry mainstream by the sheer numbers of professionals who wish to join our team precisely because of our culture. If your company is struggling with employee retention, employee satisfaction, or having a difficult time recruiting "A" players, you have no choice but to consider employing a culture of transparency.

At PagnatoKarp, we created a culture of transparency by simply following the **6Ts of Exponential Transparency**. If we can do it, you can too!

1 TRANSPARENCY STANDARDS—

Created ten True Fiduciary® standards focused on stripping out conflicts of interest that exist in the wealth management industry.

2 TERMS—

Client pays PagnatoKarp one fee for our services. This is the only source of revenue the firm receives—very simple, transparent terms.

3 TOTAL ACCOUNTABILITY—

PagnatoKarp provides the U.S. Securities and Exchange Commission (SEC) our True Fiduciary® standards and is held accountable by SEC federal regulators. Also, every PagnatoKarp employee attests every year to following all ten standards and is held accountable.

4 TRANSPARENT COST—

Transparently disclose every dollar received to our family office clients. Our clients know exactly what they are paying every quarter.

5 TRUTH—

The PagnatoKarp brand and culture embodies truth. We are a True Fiduciary® company, a Fiduciary Business®, and the only wealth management firm capable of stating this.

6 TRUST—

The 6Ts of Exponential Transparency provide the opportunity for clients to "trust" PagnatoKarp.

TRANSPARENCY CHANGES EVERYTHING !!

PERSPECTIVES

cul·ture

/ˈkəlCHər/

the customs, arts, social institutions, and achievements of a particular nation, people, or other social group.

WHY **IT MATTERS:**

- Transparency drives culture. As the founder of Starbucks eloquently stated, "The most important thing for any business is the people; without the people, a business has nothing."

- Individual transparency is a building block toward an overall culture of transparency.

ADVICE:

- Employees that are "A" players will demand a culture of transparency. Remember this if you're struggling with employee retention, employee satisfaction, or recruiting "A" players.

- If you lead by example and demonstrate your unique abilities, you will find the path that gives you the most fulfillment.

- Follow the 6Ts of Exponential Transparency.

TAKE**AWAYS**:

- All 7 billion people on the planet have a "unique ability," and everyone's is different.

- The world's greatest corporate leaders, philanthropists, and thinkers have made a culture of transparency a priority.

- Transparency and decentralization go hand in hand.

ACTION STEPS:

- Make sure your level of energy, creativity, and focus is on point. The key to exponential growth lies in having a positive attitude.

- Figure out your Massive Transformative Purpose (MTP).

- Read Exponential Organizations by Salim Ismail.

- Seek contributions from all members of your team.

"Transparency is beautiful and is here to stay."

Paul Pagnato

CHAPTER 25

Riding the Transparency Wave

By now, you should understand that my mantra of "Positive Mental Attitude" and maximized transparency are not only complementary, but they exist in lockstep as the guiding principles of my life. I don't compartmentalize or alter the underlying belief to adapt to family, leisure, or business. They're one and the same. Success and happiness are the result of that consistency.

Working on this project for over two years has not only been thrilling, but it has literally lit up my life and my excitement for future endeavors. Each new inquiry, each new idea, and each new chapter could have spawned a dozen more.

It has also forced me to revisit some of the concerns that keep me up at night, and to figure how to best address them. Some of those could be world-changing, while others might affect only my family or even just a small corner of my life. It has led me to a place of greater clarity and of a lens that I'm positive provides me with 20/20 vision. I may not always make what others see as the right decision, but I'm confident when I reach an inflection point, it's the result of careful, thorough, and remarkably objective processes.

It has also given me a framework with which to tackle future challenges. Society and technology wait for no single individual; what I see as truths or likelihoods today could be radically impacted and altered by some unforeseeable events, but my focus on transparency provides a "superpower." The ability to adapt, to pivot and dig in when that's the right thing to do.

By exploring the 6Ts of Exponential Transparency, you now have a flowchart by which to consider every aspect of your life and the world. When some decision or some mixture of priorities threatens to paralyze your analytical abilities, simply cycle through each "T," one at a time, and discern the outcome or the thought tree that provides the greatest overall return. Sometimes you'll have to prioritize one over another. It's not always an easy paradigm to adopt, but the process is as important as the result. If you follow the process, you'll reach the optimal result more often than not.

Eventually, you won't need to employ each "T" so consciously. Rather than going through all of them sequentially and divining an outcome, your brain will exercise a sort of "muscle memory" that allows you to go through the sequence in rapid succession. This is a wave, so the most fitting analogy would seem to be surfing. When you first get out on a surfboard, each part of your body has a job to do, and you control them independently.

What are your hips doing?

Is your core strong?

Where are your feet positioned?

Are your knees bent to absorb any impact?

Are your hands providing you with balance?

Are you looking for a rogue wave?

It takes time to get all these parts working cohesively. You'll likely take several spills when one part of your body lets you down.

Eventually, though, you won't have to think about what each part of the team is doing. Your hips will be positioned properly, and your knees will react fluidly. Your core won't let you down. Your feet and hands will balance you out. And your eyes will process subtle environmental changes before they're apparent to anyone else. Think of each of those body parts as a single "T."

You'll go from unbalanced to confident before you know it.

The wave is here. Enjoy the ride.

TRANSPARENCY CHANGES EVERYTHING !!

6Ts of Exponential
TRANSPARENCY

6 TRUST

5 TRUTH

4 TRANSPARENT COST

3 TOTAL ACCOUNTABILITY

2 TERMS

1 TRANSPARENCY STANDARDS

Transparency Changes **Everything.**

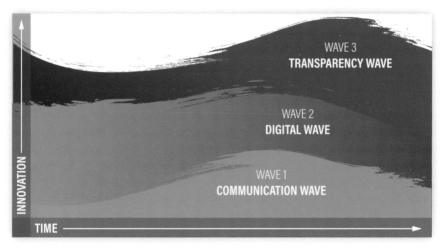

THE THREE WAVES OF **INNOVATION**

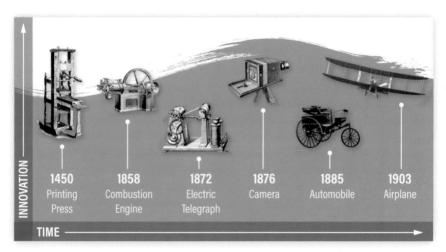

THE FIRST WAVE OF INNOVATION: **COMMUNICATION WAVE**

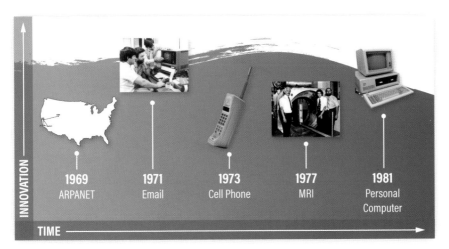

THE SECOND WAVE OF INNOVATION: **DIGITAL WAVE**

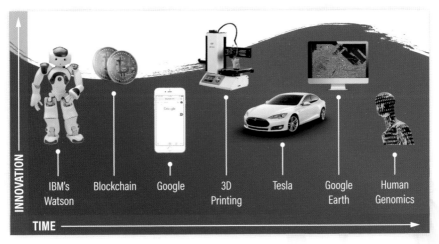

THE THIRD WAVE OF INNOVATION: **TRANSPARENCY WAVE**

It's Time to **Ride the Wave!**

PERSPECTIVES

CHAPTER 25 | RIDING THE TRANSPARENCY WAVE

am·bas·sa·dor

/amˈbasədər/

a person who acts as a representative
or promoter of a specified activity.

TELL YOUR STORY

LIVE TRANSPARENTLY

TRANSPARENCY
AMBASSADOR

CHANGE YOUR LIFE

BE BETTER THAN THAT

WHY **IT MATTERS:**

- Success and happiness are the residue of consistency. Don't compartmentalize your life—strive for transparency and Positive Mental Attitude (PMA) across the board.

ADVICE:

- Use the 6Ts of Exponential Transparency as a flow chart for every aspect of your life.
- Enable the 6Ts to become an unconscious extension of your brain.

TAKE**AWAYS:**

- Transparency Changes EVERYTHING !!
- Personal transparency is the key to unlocking fear and obstacles.
- The wave is here—enjoy the ride.

ACTION STEPS**:**

- Practice PMA every day.
- Share your personal transparency story with others and become a Transparency Ambassador.

BECOME A TRANSPARENCY AMBASSADOR... SHARE YOUR STORY TODAY!

#transparencywave

APPENDIX 1

By Professor Yaniv Konchitchki, UC Berkeley

The importance of transparency in the real world is also notable when considering the U.S. capital markets, as reflected from recent cutting-edge research. Specifically, a recent research study demonstrates that greater transparency in corporate's earnings has a positive effect on the bottom line, thus making a case for more transparent financial information provided by Corporate America.

The research, entitled "Cost of Capital and Earnings Transparency" and published in a top-tier academic journal (Journal of Accounting and Economics, Volume 55, Issue 1-2, Pages 206-224, with a DOI at http://dx.doi.org/10.1016/j.jacceco.2013.01.004), focuses on the linkage between the transparency of a corporate's financial statements and its discount rate (also called cost of equity capital). The paper is co-authored by Professors Yaniv Konchitchki (University of California at Berkeley's Haas School of Business), Mary Barth (Stanford University's Graduate School of Business), and Wayne Landsman (University of North Carolina at Chapel Hill's Kenan-Flagler Business School).

The paper provides theory and finds evidence that U.S. corporations that are more transparent in their accounting earnings information enjoy higher stock valuations (through lower discount rates). More specifically, "a corporate's value is often determined by discounting future cash flows by the corporate's cost of capital," as Professor Yaniv Konchitchki from University of California at Berkeley explains. Cost of capital is defined as the rate of return that capital could be expected to earn in an alternative investment of equivalent risk. It is used to evaluate new projects within a company to give investors information and assurance of a minimum return for providing capital.

The research finds that a corporate's cost of capital is negatively related to its financial transparency. In other words, when there is less earnings transparency, the risk to investors is higher, resulting in higher cost of capital. Likewise, if there is more earnings transparency, one has access to more information about a company's value by observing its earnings, resulting in lower risk and, in turn, lower cost of capital. Ultimately, lower cost of capital equates to higher valuation of a firm's stocks.

In addition to the above, the research provides two notable innovations. One is that this study is the first to provide an economic mechanism that directly links an empirical accounting quality measure to cost of capital, through the channel of information asymmetry—an important contribution to the research literature. The second innovation is that this paper uses cost of capital measures that are not affected by common biases such as those stemming from using growth forecasts or analyst earnings forecasts to derive implied cost of capital measures that were often used in the literature. This paper was recently selected as the Best Paper Award by the American Accounting Association, *"judged to best reflect the tradition of academic scholarship and be of relevance to problems facing the accounting profession and standard-setters,"* as quoted by this award.

"This research changes how we consider the quality of financial data from corporate financial statements, because the evidence in this paper illuminates how important transparent accounting is for stock valuation," Professor Konchitchki says.

Consider, for example, a case of Alphabet Inc. (NASDAQ: GOOG), with earnings (i.e., net income, which was equal to its earnings before discontinued operations and extraordinary items) of $30,736 million and $12,662 million for the fiscal years ended on December 31, 2018 and June 30, 2017, respectively, as well as stock return for the year ended in December 31, 2018 of 2.32% [=(1070.71 − 1046.40)/1046.40; Source: Google Finance). Suppose also that earnings are defined as E and stock return is defined as RET. Then, earnings transparency is the sum of the industry component and the industry-neutral component. In particular, these transparency components are the adjusted R^2s from annual regressions of returns, RET, for year t on earnings before discontinued operations and extraordinary items, deflated by lagged price, E/P_{t-1}, and change in earnings, deflated by lagged price, $\Delta E/P_{t-1}$, by industry and by portfolio based on the quartile of the residual from the industry regressions, respectively.

Let us now suppose that, for example, Alphabet Inc.'s earnings transparency for 2018 is 42%. Roughly it means (ignoring the two components comprising the total transparency measure) that observing the earnings of Alphabet enables explaining 40% of the stock return variation of Alphabet Inc.'s stock price.

The natural question then is: Why would earnings transparency be associated with stock valuation? Indeed, the research (again, titled "Cost of Capital and Earnings Transparency" and published by the Journal of Accounting and Economics) predicts and finds that earnings transparency is negatively associated with cost of capital (and thus to stock valuation). The basic economic intuition is the well-established positive relation between information asymmetry and cost of capital and the paper's expectation that earnings transparency is negatively associated with information asymmetry. As the paper explains: "We expect a negative relation between earnings transparency and information asymmetry because when earnings transparency is low, some investors will engage in private information acquisition. Acquiring information about a firm's economic value beyond that reflected in earnings—which is low cost information about firm value—is costly. When this cost varies across investors, investors will differ in the extent to which they acquire information, which contributes to information asymmetry. Also, information asymmetry among investors can vary across firms such that it is negatively associated with transparency if investors' marginal acquisition costs are higher when there is less information about firm value beyond that reflected in earnings. However, ultimately it is an empirical question whether transparency is cross-sectionally negatively associated with information asymmetry. To the extent that earnings transparency is not negatively associated with information asymmetry, we will be unlikely to find a significant negative relation between earnings transparency and cost of capital."

The next natural question is: Why would transparency vary among firms and over time? As also explained in the paper, there are several sources of cross-sectional variation in earnings transparency. One is that earnings are not designed to reflect all changes in economic value. For example, the accounting system is not designed to capture economic benefits associated with expected future contracts from current customer relationships. The second is that the accounting system does not uniformly measure earnings in a manner that reflects changes in economic value. Also, the way in which earnings maps into firm value can differ across firms for a variety of reasons that are not necessarily directly related to accounting. In addition, because of differences in incentives managers face, firms differ in the amount of discretion their managers apply opportunistically.

As the paper also explains, "similarly, there are several sources of intertemporal variation in earnings transparency, which we expect to lead to economically meaningful variation in the cost of capital. One source is changes in accounting standards. For example, Statement of Financial Accounting Standards No. 133 (SFAS 133, FASB, 1998) requires recognition of derivative financial instruments that affects earnings, but recognition of these instruments was not required prior to SFAS 133. A second source is changes in the mix of a firm's assets. For example, until recently many insurance companies' assets and liabilities related only to insurance policies, but recently these companies have also invested in credit default swaps. As a result, insurance companies' asset mix changed and so likely did their earnings transparency. A third source is that, because of these changes or other reasons, e.g., changes in the clarity of firms' disclosures, the mapping of earnings into firm value can differ over time. Because there is cross-sectional variation in transparency, the effects of these intertemporal changes are likely to affect different firms differently."

NOTES

ABOUT THE AUTHOR

1   PagnatoKarp AUA as of 1/31/20. AUA = Assets under advisement refers to assets on which the firm provides advice or consultation but for which the firm either has discretionary authority or does not arrange or effectuate the transaction.

2   PagnatoKarp disclosures: https://www.pagnatokarp.com/disclosures/

CHAPTER 1: WAVES OF THE PAST AND FUTURE

1   Feloni, Richard, "Billionaire investor Steve Case said a book he read in 1980 set him on the path to founding AOL, and it still influences him today." Yahoo Finance (October 12, 2018). Retrieved from https://finance.yahoo.com/news/billionaire-investor-steve-case-said-125800126.html

CHAPTER 2: THE COMMUNICATION WAVE

1   Moore, Robert J., "Eric Schmidt's "5 Exabytes" Quote is a Load of Crap." TheDataPoint (February 7, 2011). Retrieved from https://blog.rjmetrics.com/2011/02/07/eric-schmidts-5-exabytes-quote-is-a-load-of-crap/

CHAPTER 3: THE DIGITAL WAVE

1   In 2015, Brian Krzanich, the former CEO of Intel, announced that "Our cadence today is closer to two and a half years than two." Borwein, Jonathan, "Moore's Law is now 50 years old, but will it continue?" Science Alert (July 24, 2015). Retrieved from https://www.sciencealert.com/moore-s-law-is-now-50-years-old-but-will-it-continue

2   Bela Nagy, J. Doyne Farmer, Quan M. Bui, Jessika E. Trancik, "Statistical Basis for Predicting Technological Progress." Plos One (February 28, 2013). Retrieved from https://journals.plos.org/plosone/article?id=10.1371/journal.pone.0052669

3   Handy, Jim, "Moore's Law vs. Wright's Law." Forbes (March 25, 2013). Retrieved from https://www.forbes.com/sites/jimhandy/2013/03/25/moores-law-vs-wrights-law/#7bf6d70577d2

4   Kurweil, Ray, "The Law of Accelerating Returns." Kurzweil accelerating intelligence (March 7, 2001). Retrieved from https://www.kurzweilai.net/the-law-of-accelerating-returns

5   Bates Ramirez, Vanessa, "The 6 Ds of Tech Disruption: A Guide to the Digital Economy." Singularity Hub (November 22, 2016). Retrieved from https://singularityhub.com/2016/11/22/the-6-ds-of-tech-disruption-a-guide-to-the-digital-economy/

6   Block, Ryan, "Palm's Ed Colligan Laughs Off iPhone." Engadget.com (November 21, 2006. Retrieved from https://www.engadget.com/2006/11/21/palms-ed-colligan-laughs-off-iphone/

7   Tony, "Happy birthday iPhone: it's now 10 years since Apple started a revolution." Business Insider (January 9, 2017). Retrieved from https://www.businessinsider.com.au/happy-birthday-iphone-its-now-10-years-since-apple-started-a-revolution-2017-1

CHAPTER 4 THE TRANSPARENCY WAVE

1   Ohlheiser, Abby, "The woman behind 'Me Too' knew the power of the phrase when she created it – 10 years ago." The Washington Post (October 19, 2017). Retrieved from https://www.washingtonpost.com/news/the-intersect/wp/2017/10/19/the-woman-behind-me-too-knew-the-power-of-the-phrase-when-she-created-it-10-years-ago/

2   Wong, Curtis M., "Terry Crews: Me Too Movement 'Is the Emancipation Proclamation.'" Huffington Post (May 16, 2018). Retrieved from https://www.huffingtonpost.com/entry/terry-crews-safe-horizon-award_us_5afc4745e4b0a59b4dff8f9c

CHAPTER 6 THE DEFINING ISSUE GOING FORWARD

1   Barbaschow, Asha, "Why open source is so important to Microsoft." ZDNet (February 28, 2018). Retrieved from https://www.zdnet.com/article/why-open-source-is-so-important-to-microsoft/

2   Vaughan-Nichols, Steven J., "Microsoft open-sources its patent portfolio." ZDNet (October 10, 2018). Retrieved from https://www.zdnet.com/article/microsoft-open-sources-its-entire-patent-portfolio/

3   Ibid.

4   Ibid.

CHAPTER 7 PERCEPTIONS

1   O'Brien, Matt, "Did 2018 usher in a creeping tech dystopia?" AP News (December 24, 2018). Retrieved from https://www.apnews.com/32d7fa7625044044950053a793448ee0

2   Ibid

CHAPTER 8 GENERATIONAL SHIFT

1   Greenstein, Tracey, "Top 5 Free Finance Apps." Forbes (October 20, 2011). Retrieved from https://www.forbes.com/sites/traceygreenstein/2011/10/10/the-top-5-free-finance-apps/#21cacdad2068

CHAPTER 9 GET READY FOR THE RIDE OF YOUR LIFE

1   Source 2018 Transparency International Organization

2   Data provided by ARK Investments LLC

CHAPTER 13 LONGEVITY AND OPPORTUNITIES

1   TIME magazine (February 12, 2015). Retrieved from https://time.com/3706775/in-the-latest-issue-23/

CHAPTER 15 LONGEVITY DEMANDS A PLAN

1   Gent, Edd, "Eternal Life Is No Good Without Eternal Youth." Singularity Hub (September 10, 2018). Retrieved from https://singularityhub.com/2018/09/10/eternal-life-is-no-good-without-eternal-youth/

2   "List of the verified oldest people." Wikipedia (September 12, 2019). Retrieved from https://en.wikipedia.org/wiki/List_of_the_verified_oldest_people

3   Buettner, Dan, "Reverse Engineering Longevity." Blue Zones® (Accessed May 1, 2019). Retrieved from https://www.bluezones.com/2016/11/power-9/

4   Ibid

5   Fa, Shelly, "Have We Reached the Limit of Human Longevity? New Study Says No." Singularity Hub (July 3, 2018. Retrieved from https://singularityhub.com/2018/07/03/have-we-reached-the-limit-of-human-longevity-new-study-says-no/#sm.00176a7sf1br4efew1v16h2qddjso

6   "Longevity and Transparency: Hand In Hand." PagnatoKarp (November 16, 2018). Retrieved from https://www.pagnatokarp.com/longevity-and-transparency-hand-in-hand/

7   Fosco, Molly, "How Your Genes Could Be Used To Cure Cancer." Ozy, The Daily Dose (August 9, 2018). Retrieved from https://www.ozy.com/fast-forward/how-your-genes-could-be-used-to-cure-cancer/87773

8   Ibid

9   Ibid

CHAPTER 18 CUTTING-EDGE TECHNOLOGIES: BLOCKCHAIN

1   https://motherboard.vice.com/en_us/article/j5nzx4/what-was-the-first-blockchain

2   See http://www.fooledbyrandomness.com/. See also, Bates Ramirez, Vanessa, "How Cryptocurrencies Can Influence the Future of Freedom." Singularity Hub (August 27, 2018). Retrieved from https://singularityhub.com/2018/08/27/why-cryptocurrencies-are-crucial-to-the-future-of-freedom/#sm.00176a7sf1br4efew1v16h2qddjso.

3 See, e.g., http://www.atimes.com/article/the-history-of-price-bubbles-shows-how-low-bitcoin-could-go/. See also Wolf, Janine, "Bitcoin in the greatest bubble in history, bigger than tulips, the South Se Company and gold – and now it's popping." Bloomberg News (April 10, 2018). Retrieved from https://business.financialpost.com/technology/blockchain/bitcoin-seen-popping-like-the-greatest-bubbles-by-bofa

4 La Monica, Paul R., "Warren Buffett says Bitcoin is 'rat poison.'" CNN Business (May 8, 2018). Retrieved from https://money.cnn.com/2018/05/07/investing/warren-buffett-bitcoin/index.html

5 Ibid

6 Wikipedia https://en.wikipedia.org/wiki/Hyperinflation_in_Zimbabwe

CHAPTER 20 FINANCIAL CRISIS

1 PagnatoKarp disclosures: https://www.pagnatokarp.com/disclosures/

2 "The Effects of Conflicted Advice on Retirement Savings", February 2015, The Council of Economic Advisers, within the Executive Office of the President of the United States.

3 Ibid

CHAPTER 21 WEALTH ABUNDANCE

1 PagnatoKarp AUA as of 1/31/20. AUA = Assets under advisement refers to assets on which the firm provides advice or consultation but for which the firm either has discretionary authority or does not arrange or effectuate the transaction.

CHAPTER 22 TRANSPARENCY BEASTS

1 Konchitchki, Yaniv, Barth, Mary, and Landsman, Wayne, "Cost of Capital and Earnings Transparency", Journal of Accounting & Economics (JAE), Forthcoming Stanford University Graduate School of Business Research Paper No. 2015 Rock Center for Corporate Governance at Stanford University Working Paper No. 48 (Revised May 14, 2013)

CHAPTER 23 PERSONAL TRANSPARENCY

1 Luciani, Joseph, "Why 80 Percent of New Year's Resolutions Fail." US News & World Report (December 29, 2015). Retrieved from https://health.usnews.com/health-news/blogs/eat-run/articles/2015-12-29/why-80-percent-of-new-years-resolutions-fail

PHOTO CREDITS

Cover   Author Photo, Melissa Demple Photography

Intro   *Don Adams with Shoe Phone*, (cc), Wikimedia

Intro   *Vintage TV*, makamuki0, pixabay.com

Ch 1   *Alvin Toffler. Taken at Beverly Hills*, California. (cc), Wikimedia

Ch 1   *Ocean Wave*, Mark Harpur @luckybeanz, unsplash.com

Ch 2   *Power Loom Weaving*, The IK Workshop Society at www.ikfoundation.org

Ch 2   *Printer in 1568, Meggs, Philip B., A History of Graphic Design* (cc), Wikimedia

Ch 3   *Gordon Moore* (cc), https://www.intel.com/pressroom/kits/events/moores_law_40th/

Ch 3   *John C. (Jack) Bogle (1929-2019), The Institute for Fiduciary Standard (cc)*, Wikimedia

Ch 3   *Peter Diamandis*, Michael Buckner/Getty Images for Pernod Ricard

Ch 3   *Skyline Drive*, Vlad Tchompalov @tchompalov, unsplash.com

Ch 4   *Armenia*, Gor Davtyan @gor918, unsplash.com

Ch 4   *Blue Waterdrop*, Herbert Goetsch @hg_photo, unsplash.com

Ch 4   *Elderly Couple*, Micheile Henderson @micheile, unsplash.com

Ch 4   *Feet in Hammock*, Ēriks Irmejs @erxxx, unsplash.com

Ch 4   *Money*, Mackenzie Marco @kenziem, unsplash.com

Ch 4   *Old Books*, freestocks @freestocks, unsplash.com

Ch 4   *Soldier with Shoes*, skeeze, pixabay.com

Ch 5   *Marc Benioff*, (cc) Kenneth Yeung - www.thelettertwo.com

Ch 5   *Tandem Paragliding*, Eun-Kwang Bae @unplanner, unsplash.com

Ch 6   *Facebook Ceo Mark Zuckerberg Testifies In Front Of Us Congress*, dreamstime.com

Ch 6   *Social Media Earth*, geralt, pixabay.com

Ch 7   *Bristol Robotics Laboratory*, Louis Reed @_louisreed, unsplash.com

Ch 7   *New York City*, Juliana Malta @julianamalta, unsplash.com

Ch 7   *Sandstone Antelope Canyon*, Sebastien Gabriel @sgabriel, unsplash.com

Ch 8   *Epidermal Electronic System*, John A. Rogers, https://theconversation.com

Ch 8   *iPhone X Weather Theme App*, Maulik Sutariya @truemaulik, unsplash.com

Ch 9   *Baby Feet*, Ignacio Campo @ignaciocampo, unsplash.com

Ch 9   *Crossing*, Arturo Castaneyra @castaneyra, unsplash.com

Ch 9   *Fishing*, Jim Degerstrom, pixabay.com

Ch 9   *Heart Printed on a 3-D Printer*, Evgeny Gerasimov, dreamstime.com

Ch 9   *Robot Finger, Keyboard*, Geralt, pixabay.com

Ch 9   *Square*, Nathan Dumlao @nate_dumlao, unsplash.com

Ch 9   *Sunrise Surfer*, Frank McKenna @frankiefoto, unsplash.com

Ch 9   *Tesla Dash*, Bram Van Oost @ort, unsplash.com

Ch 9   *Tesla P100D Cockpit*, Roberto Nickson @rpnickson, unsplash.com

Ch 9   *US Capitol*, Bob Bowie @connave, unsplash.com

Ch 10   *Full Disk Earth, Appollo 17, 1972*, The New York Public Library @nypl, unsplash.com (edited)

Ch 10   *Portrait of Albert Einstein*, (cc), Wikimedia

Ch 10   *The Trouble with Tribbles*, Photo, CBS, Getty Images

Ch 10   *What a Night*, Klemen Vrankar @vklemen, unsplash.com

Ch 11   *Communication City*, Tumisu, pixabay.com

Ch 12   *Back To The Future Delorean Space Vortex Travel*, Photodynamx, dreamstime.com

Ch 12   *Kodiak Bears*, skeeze, pixabay.com

Ch 12   *Salvelinus malma malma (Dolly Varden Trout)* (cc), Wikimedia

Ch 12   *Snorkel trip off the Coast of Oahu*, Jakob Owens @jakobowens1, unsplash.com

Ch 13   *Baby Minimal White Background by Bed*, Henley Design Studio @henleydesign, unsplash.com

Ch 13 *Jeanne Calment*, Photo from Dr. Stacey Naito's Blog, Creative Commons License, https://thedeclarationatcoloniahigh.com/

Ch 14 *Jack Andraka, Inventor* (cc), Wikimedia

Ch 14 *Microbiology*, PublicDomainPictures, pixabay.com

Ch 14 *Running*, Filip Mroz @mroz, unsplash.com

Ch 15 *Furuzamami Beach in Zamami Island (Okinawa) in Japan*, Roméo A. @gronemo, unsplash.com

Ch 15 *Greek Church*, Russell_Yan, pixabay.com

Ch 15 *Loma Linda University Medical Center*, (cc), Wikimedia

Ch 15 *Playa Conchal, Costa Rica*, Lindsay Loucel @linds_loucel, unsplash.com

Ch 16 *Floating in Zakynthos, Greece*, Štefan Štefančík @cikstefan, unsplash.com

Ch 16 *Hand with Cell Phone*, Charles Deluvio @charlesdeluvio, unsplash.com

Ch 16 *Keys in Hand*, Tumisu, pixabay.com

Ch 16 *Login*, TBIT, pixabay.com

Ch 16 *Mix of vegetables at the Flower Show in Chantilly*, Chantal Garnier @chantalgarnier, unsplash.com

Ch 17 *AI Collage*, geralt, pixabay.com

Ch 17 *Alexa*, Waldemar Brandt @waldemarbrandt67w, unsplash.com

Ch 17 *Deep Blue* (cc), https://commons.wikimedia.org/wiki/File:Deep_Blue.jpg

Ch 17 *Drone*, Jared Brashier @jaredbrasier, unsplash.com

Ch 17 *Garry Kasparov*, (cc), Wikimedia

Ch 17 *IBM's Watson*, (cc), Wikimedia

Ch 17 *Nordic Walker with Smartphone*, Antonio Grosz @angro, unsplash.com

Ch 17 *Smart Home*, Pixaline, pixabay.com

Ch 17 *Uber*, Charles Deluvio @charlesdeluvio, unsplash.com

Ch 17 *Young Man Wearing Apple Watch*, Luke Chesser @lukechesser, unsplash.com

Ch 18 *Airbnb*, InstagramFOTOGRAFIN, pixabay.com

Ch 18 *Cryptocurrency*, WorldSpectrum, pixabay.com

Ch 18 *Market*, Austin Distel @austindistel www.distel.co, unsplash.com

Ch 18 *The Obverse of the 2009 Zimbabwe $100 trillion banknote* (cc), Wikimedia

Ch 18 *Total US Venture Capital Investments* (cc), Wikimedia

Ch 18 *ZWD vs USD Exchange Rate History* (cc), Wikimedia

Ch 19 *Hot Air Balloons*, Daniel Akre @strawhouse, unsplash.com

Ch 19 *Summit of Aiako Harria*, Spain, Julentto Photography @julensan09, unsplash.com

Ch 20 *Tom, Feeling the Love*, David Morris, flickr.com

Ch 20 *GDP Real Growth in 2009* (cc), Wikimedia

Ch 20 *Seal of the United States Securities and Exchange Commission* (cc), Wikimedia

Ch 20 *The seal of the United States Department of Labor* (cc), Wikimedia

Ch 21 *Fields of Grain*, Jordan McQueen @jordanfmcqueen, unsplash.com

Ch 21 *Man Using Smartphone While Driving*, SplitShire, pexels.com

Ch 22 *Partners Statue at the Disneyland Resort, J Boncodin*, dreamstime.com

Ch 23 *Birds, San Diego Beach*, Frank McKenna @frankiefoto, unsplash.com

Ch 23 *Chess Strategy*, jarmoluk, pixabay.com

Ch 23 *Sticky Note*, OpenClipart-Vectors, pixabay.com

Ch 24 *Balance*, Derzulya Zaza @derzulya, unsplash.com

Ch 24 *Connection*, PublicDomainPictures, pixabay.com

Ch 24 *Mountain Scape*, Conrad Liebowitz @conrad, ron, unsplash.com

Ch 24 *We Did It!*, Natalie Pedigo @nataliepedigo, unsplash.com

SHARE YOUR STORY!

BECOME A TRANSPARENCY
AMBASSADOR!

#transparencywave

transparencywave.com